MISSION STATEMENT

To empower and give HOPE to
everyone from the financially
distressed to the financially secure.

Published by THE LAMPO GROUP, INC.
For more information, please contact DAVE RAMSEY's office at
1.888.22PEACE

LISTEN TO "THE DAVE RAMSEY SHOW" 24 HOURS/DAY, 7 DAYS/WEEK anywhere in the world! www.daveramsey.com

About the Founder of FPU:

Dave Ramsey is a personal money management expert, an extremely popular national radio personality and best-selling author of *The Total Money Makeover*. In his latest book, a follow-up of his enormously successful *New York Times* best sellers *Financial Peace* and *More Than Enough*, Ramsey exemplifies his life's work of teaching others how to be financially responsible so they can acquire enough wealth to take care of loved ones, live prosperously into old age, and give generously to others.

Ramsey knows first-hand what financial peace means in his own life – living a true riches to rags to riches story. By age 26 he had established a $4 million real estate portfolio, only to lose it by age 30. He has since rebuilt his financial life and now devotes himself full-time to helping ordinary people understand the forces behind their financial distress and how to set things right – financially, emotionally and spiritually.

Ramsey offers life-changing financial advice as a host of a nationally syndicated radio program *The Dave Ramsey Show*, which is heard by more than 2 million listeners each week on more than 250 radio stations throughout the United States.

Ramsey is the creator of Financial Peace University (FPU), a 13-week program that helps people dump their debt, get control of their money, and learn new behaviors around money that are founded on commitment and accountability. More than 260,000 families have attended FPU classes at their workplace, church, military base, local nonprofit organization, Spanish organization, or community group. Many national corporations have used and benefited from the program as well. The average family pays off $5,300 in debt and saves $2,700 in the first 91 days after beginning FPU and is completely out of debt, except for the mortgage, in 18 to 24 months.

Ramsey created a group of products in an effort to teach children about money before they have a chance to make mistakes. Financial Peace for the Next Generation is an all inclusive school curriculum that is currently in more than 300 schools across the country. Financial Peace Jr. is an instructional kit designed to help parents teach their young children about working, saving and giving their money. Through Ramsey's entertaining children's book series future millionaires learn financial lessons early.

Ramsey earned his Bachelor of Science degree in Finance and Real Estate from the University of Tennessee. A frequent speaker around the country at large-scale live events, Ramsey is a passionate and inspiring presenter who is at ease on both sides of the mike. More than 300,000 people have attended Ramsey's LIVE events.

He resides with his wife, Sharon, and their three children, Denise, Rachel, and Daniel, in Nashville, Tennessee.

Resources

With this kit, you have *a lifetime membership* in this *life-changing* program.

▶ If you have not already enrolled in a class, please visit www.daveramsey.com or contact our office at 1.888.22PEACE to find a location near you. Group accountability is essential to gaining financial peace.

▶ Check out all our products in our online store.

▶ Find out how you can become a coordinator and/or help bring Financial Peace University to your community, church or business. Simply complete the FPU Coordinator Form or call our office at 1.888.227.3223.

Need More Help?

▶ Certified Counselors are *professionals* that Dave's team has *trained* to help serve *your financial needs*.

From a tune-up for the financially healthy to challenge sessions for families facing creditors or even bankruptcy, these sessions can provide HOPE and tools for financial success.

Visit www.daveramsey.com and click on the COUNSELING button or call 1.888.227.3223 for more information.

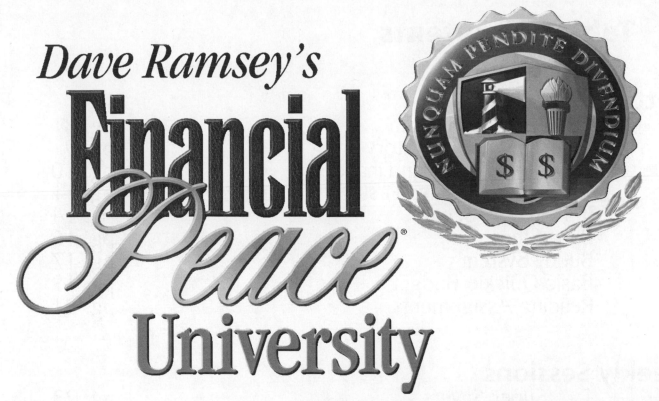

✓ Table of Contents

Getting Started

Weekly Sessions

Educational Materials Available

Glossary

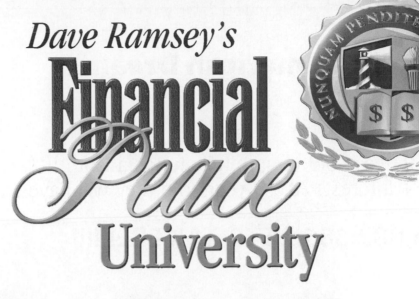

Dave Ramsey's
Financial Peace University

Getting Started

Travis Foster

"A man's heart plans his way, but the Lord directs his steps."
Proverbs 16:9 (NKJV)

✔ The American Dream

Imagine if...

A 30-year-old couple fully funds a Roth IRA ($500 per month) at 12% interest. At 70 years old they will have . . .

$5,882,386.26 . . . TAX FREE!!!!

Imagine if...

That same 30-year-old couple made $40,000 and saved 15% in a 401(k) ($6,000.00 per year, $500.00 per month - at 12% interest). At 70 years old they will have . . .

$5,882,386.26 . . . in the 401(k)

By Retirement

That 30-year-old couple, DEBT FREE, saves $1,000 per month at 12% interest. At 70 years old, they will have:

Roth IRA	**$5,882,386.26**
401k	**$5,882,386.26**
Total	**$11,764,772.51**

...and to think this could be **you**.

IF YOU WILL LIVE LIKE NO ONE ELSE, LATER YOU CAN LIVE LIKE NO ONE ELSE.

The Amazing Free Car Story

We normally buy:

$18,000 car with payments of $300 for 7 years at 10%.
Value after 7 years = $800.

Or we could buy instead:

$6,000 car with payments of $100 for 7 years at 10%.
Value after 7 years = $400.

The other $200 pcr month saved at 10% for 7 years = $24,190

NOW WHO MADE THE CORRECT CHOICE ?!?!!

<u>At Year Seven</u>
The car is junk, in either plan, but in our plan:

Savings	$24,190
One-year-old car for cash	$16,000
Left in savings	$ 8,190

No Car Payments!

<u>Another Seven Years</u>
Save $300 per month from year 7 to year 14, plus
Interest on $8,190 (10% return), the car is junk again.

Savings	$52,245
One-year-old car for cash	$25,000
Left in savings	$27,245

No Car Payments!

So here we go again!

We will have free cars the rest of our lives just because we purchased a lower priced car one time 14 years ago.

getting started

✔ Snapshots of American Finances

According to the *Wall Street Journal*, nearly 70% of all consumers live from **paycheck to paycheck**.

Of all filings, according to the American Bankruptcy Institute, typical bankruptcy filings are over 1,300,000 annually with a new record being set virtually every year (almost 1.6 million in 2004). Personal bankruptcies account for 97% and 70% are "total" bankruptcy -- that is, Chapter 7 where you have nothing left -- and 95% of those cases are declared "no asset" by the courts.

According to a Gallop poll in *USA Today*, those polled say they aren't laughing all the way to bankruptcy court like they thought they would. In fact, **75%** of filers felt **depressed** after going through a bankruptcy.

Christian Financial Concepts says that in **1929 only 2%** of the homes in America had a mortgage against them, and by **1962 only 2% DID NOT** have a mortgage against them.

Consumer Reports Money Book says the typical household has **$38,000** in debt and that total consumer debt has almost tripled since 1980. In 1980 the total consumer debt was $1.3 trillion and now is over $3.3 trillion.

A Marist Institute poll published in *USA Today* stated that **55%** of Americans "always" or "sometimes" **worry** about their money.

Nearly half of all Americans **(46%) have less than $10,000 saved for their retirement**, according to Miles To Go: A Status Report on Americans' Plans for Retirement, a new public opinion study released by Public Agenda.

In the new millenium, the personal savings rate fell to around **-2.2% -- the lowest in 60 years**, according to the Department of Commerce.

According to Automatic Data Processing, Inc., **20% of workers** would **not** be able to make a mortgage, utility or credit card payment if they missed a paycheck.

At 36%, *USA Today* Snapshots reports **personal finance** as the number-one personal stress factor in the work place.

Getting Started

Getting Started

Congratulations! You have thought for years that you wanted to get ahead someday and today is the day! It is time for you to proactively take control of your finances from this day forward. A tremendous peace will come as soon as you begin developing your plan and come to the monthly realization that you are doing it.

Please take a few minutes and carefully read the following pages. By adopting the simple principles and guidelines outlined in the next few pages you will be taking the first big step toward walking in financial peace.

Putting First Things First

Personal

If you are financially secure or struggling financially, you must have a properly balanced life. Anything that is out of balance will throw your finances off. So, spiritual health, mental health, and physical health must become a priority.

Attend Church this week for a spiritual checkup.

Spend some time every morning in quiet isolation thinking about the day and what steps need to be taken that day toward your financial health. Pray and make a list of things to do.

Exercise is a wonderful way to remove stress and is obviously good for you.

Family

Spend time alone with your spouse and then with the whole family THIS WEEK!!!

If you are married, both spouses must be in agreement on all spending, saving, and debt reduction, or your plan is doomed to fail. If you are in financial stress and either will not or cannot agree on a written plan of spending BEFORE the spending occurs, you may need marriage counseling. Is that over-stated? NO!

Whether financially stressed or financially secure, you will find one of the most positive things that comes from Financial Peace University and budgeting together is that you will have a new kind of unity in your marriage -- a unity that you can only experience if you budget together.

Getting Started

Controlled by Creditors?

Are you spending your time worried about which creditor will be calling you next? We will spend some time in these thirteen sessions teaching you the details of how to pay creditors and how to handle them. In one of the accountability checklists you will learn how you can run your household instead of letting your creditors run you. The best way for them to get paid is for you to set your priorities and take control of your financial destiny.

Step One (Big Priority)

Your necessities and the well being of your family comes before your good credit rating. Pay necessities FIRST, then pay unsecured creditors with what is left.

> *"If anyone does not provide for his relatives, and especially for his immediate family, he has denied the faith and is worse than an unbeliever."*
>
> *1 Timothy 5:8 (NIV)*

Step Two (A Must)

Always communicate with your creditors, especially local ones whom you can meet in person. Huge amounts of communication will substitute for payment as long as they see you have a plan (which you will be developing).

Do NOT write any more hot or even warm checks! You need to pay debt off with the money you have been paying in bounced check charges.

Its Time to Begin!!

It is time to begin! There are nine simple things you want to remember as you begin to develop your plan.

#1—GIVE - Something wonderful happens to the human spirit and emotions when you start giving. Give at least $25 monthly to some worthy cause. Christians should be giving to their local church. Both spouses need to have a peace in prayer about giving.

> *"Honor the Lord with your possessions, and with the first fruits of all your increase..."*
>
> *Proverbs 3:9 (NKJV)*

#2—BABY STEPS - You will find the Baby Steps explained at the end of this section. We believe that you must first focus all extra money on Baby Step 1, which is to build an emergency fund. Baby Step 2 begins your debt payoff plan. All of this is explained as we go along and you work down through the Baby Steps.

#3—BUDDY SYSTEM - Another thing that you will find at the end of this section is our recommendation to find a "Buddy" with whom to work while going through Financial Peace University. This will prove to be very helpful and beneficial.

 # 4—ENVELOPE SYSTEM - Clothing, ALL food (including restaurant and miscellaneous grocery store items), and gasoline should immediately go on a pure cash-only basis. The Envelope System is provided with your membership, and details on how to begin can be found inside it's cover.

Getting Started

#5—BASIC QUICKIE BUDGET - After session one, "Super Savers," you will be putting together a brief overview of your monthly expenses. Simple instructions on how to get started are on the page entitled "Congratulations."

#6—BUDGETING - In session two, "Cash Flow Planning," Dave will teach you how to work through all of the financial management forms in that section, which include simple-to-understand samples. Every month your coordinator will be checking your zero-based budget to insure that you are trying to live by it. Be sure to bring it with you each week and, if you're married, work with your spouse.

#7—ACCOUNTABILITY - Since personal finance is 80% behavior, the class members should hold one another accountable every session! We expect to see your zero-based budget every session with next month's finished before the end of the current month. Each meeting we will review the accountability sheet for that session.

#8—FINANCIAL SNAPSHOT - After your second session, you should complete the "Session 3" column on your "Financial Snapshot" form the best you can. Fill in the column based upon what you have accomplished since you first started applying Dave Ramsey's Financial Peace principles to your life. This includes listening to *The Dave Ramsey Show* and reading *Financial Peace*. Note: Some of the questions may not apply to you at this time. Every few sessions you will fill in a column to chart your progress. Tear off the back copy after the last session and hand it in to your coordinator, keeping the top copy for yourself.

#9—READING ASSIGNMENT - Each session you will have a chapter or two that is recommended reading from *Financial Peace*. The chapter reading will correspond with the lessons that Dave teaches your class.

 **Baby Steps**

There is a process to getting out of the mess that we created without feeling overwhelmed. Getting out of debt will not happen overnight; it takes time. Here are the Baby Steps to begin the process:

Step 1: $1,000.00 in an Emergency Fund
($500.00 if income under $20,000 per year)

Step 2: Pay off all debt except the house utilizing the Debt Snowball
(found in the Dumping Debt lesson)

Step 3: Three to six months expenses in savings

Step 4: Invest 15% of household income into Roth IRAs and pre-tax retirement

Step 5: College funding

Step 6: Pay off home early

Step 7: Build wealth!
(Mutual funds, Real Estate)

Getting Started

✓ Buddy System

From our experience, we have found that many people are more successful if they utilize the "Buddy System." A buddy is another person or couple with whom to share, exchange feedback, or to bounce questions off. Many times the best support we receive is the support we give because something wonderful happens when we give.

GUIDELINES FOR THE BUDDY SYSTEM

1. Commit to one contact per month, either by a telephone call, written note or personal meeting.

2. Exchange home telephone numbers (work number at your own discretion) and addresses.

3. Buddies need to be of the same gender if you are single. Couples should be supportive as couples.

4. Your role is to provide emotional and spiritual encouragement and support. You are not expected to provide technical or mechanical financial advice. Just be there for someone.

5. Even the strongest and most intelligent among us needs an occasional push or pull, so everyone should try the Buddy System.

✓ Congratulations

YOU have taken the first step to obtaining true Financial Peace!

This program will help you get out of debt and teach you how to manage money. The Basic Quickie Budget form is to be done by tomorrow night at the latest to start your learning process.

Sit down (with your spouse, if married) and put together a basic budget (an overview) of your monthly expenses. Focus on necessities only - not debts, such as credit cards. This will help you start gaining control and confidence in handling your money and help you to see what you are spending monthly. In session two, you will learn how to do a zero-based budget.

Winners do things that make a difference.
And this will start you down the path towards winning.

There are four columns that need to be filled in:
A. <u>Monthly Total</u> column helps you see what you are spending.
  1. If you don't know the amount, put down your best estimate.
  2. If the amounts are inaccurate, you may never have actually accounted for what you have been spending in these categories.
  3. Don't worry if you are in the dark about your actual spending or if you find out you have been mismanaging your money. Just join the club.
B. The next column is the <u>Payoff Total</u> (for categories that apply).
  1. Write down how much it will take to pay off that debt.
  2. Example: Mortgage, car loans, etc.
C. The third column is <u>How Far Behind</u> are you?
  1. If you are 30 days, 60 days behind, write that down.
  2. If you are up-to-date, note that.
D. The fourth column is <u>Type Account</u>.
  1. Decide if this should come out of your checking account or if this is a category for a cash (envelope system) account.
  2. If this should be a cash account, you will have better control over it, because spending cash hurts more than writing a check.

Any item on the Quickie Budget form designated with an asterisk (*) should be a cash account.

The bottom line is simply this:
"Today, of every 100 people who reach age 65, only two are financially independent; 23 must continue working, and 75 must depend on friends, relatives or charity; of every 100 Americans reaching age 65 today, a horrifying 96 are flat broke!"

- U.S. Department of Labor

Basic Quickie Budget

DUE:
9/26/07

Get Started Today on Making a Difference in Your Financial Future

Financial Peace University

Item	Monthly Total	Payoff Total	How far Behind	Type Account
GIVING	440			
SAVING	50			
HOUSING				
First Mortgage	998	132000	—	
Second Mortgage	140	17000	—	
Repairs/Mn. Fee	50		—	
UTILITIES				
Electricity	200 ?			
Water	52			
Gas	80			
Phone	182			
Trash	—			
Cable	61			
*FOOD	800.00			CASH
TRANSPORTATION				
Car Payment	0	0		
Car Payment	0	0		
*Gas & Oil	350			CASH
*Repairs & Tires	50			
Car Insurance	296			
*CLOTHING	150.			CASH
PERSONAL				
Disability Ins.				
Health Insurance				
Life Insurance				
Child Care	—			
*Entertainment	200			CASH
OTHER MISC.	190			
allowance				
TOTAL MONTHLY NECESSITIES		Student loans?		

✔ FPU LESSON READING RECOMMENDATIONS IN *FINANCIAL PEACE REVISITED* BY DAVE RAMSEY

Recently, the personal savings rate fell to -2.2%: the lowest in 60 years, according to the Department of Commerce.

Purpose:

To help further motivate each member to start applying the principles of each lesson into their lives immediately!

Schedule:

- Weekly reading assignments to be completed after each lesson and prior to the next session.
- It is beneficial to do the reading assignments even if you have read *Financial Peace* before.
- You will find the review helpful as you go through each lesson.

Easy:

- *Financial Peace* is easy to read.
- The book was written on a seventh grade level and has been printed with large type in a style that is easy on the eyes!

Getting Started

Sessions	Reading
Getting Started **Super Savers**	**Chapter 1** - The Beginning... A Very Good Place to Start **Chapter 2** - Enough of Anything is Too Much **Chapter 3** - The Basics (A Foundation) **Chapter 10** - Pile Up Plunder
Cash Flow Planning	**Chapter 19** - Why Written? **Chapter 21** - Baby Steps
Relating With Money	**Chapter 14** - Single As a One-Dollar Bill **Chapter 15** - Tying a Knot in Your Money: Marriage **Chapter 16** - Crumb Snatchers and Money **Chapter 17** - Family, Friends, and Money **Chapter 18** - Carefully Consider Counsel
Buy Only Big, Big Bargains	**Chapter 13** - Buy Only Big, Big Bargains
Dumping Debt	**Chapter 7** - Lifestyles of the Rich **Chapter 8** - Dumping Debt
Understanding Investments	**Chapter 11** - "KISS" Your Money through subtitle/section: Simple Discipline is The Key **Chapter 12** - Of Mice and Mutual Funds through subtitle/ section: To Load Or Not To Load
Understanding Insurance	**Chapter 11** - "KISS" Your Money begin with subtitle/section: Insurance
Retirement & College Planning	**Chapter 12** - Of Mice And Mutual Funds begin with subtitle/ section: Funding Those Golden Rocking Chairs
Buyer Beware	**Chapter 5** - Let The Buyer Beware - Caveat Emptor
Real Estate & Mortgages	**Chapter 13** - Buy Only Big, Big Bargains subtitle/section: Real Estate Bargains; subtitle/section: Owner Financing Bonanza
Careers & Extra Jobs	**Chapter 6** - Career Choice
Collection Practices & Credit Bureaus	**Chapter 9** - Cucumbers, Collectors & Credit Reports **Chapter 22** - The End... Or Just The Beginning?
The Great Misunderstanding	**Chapter 4** - Understand The Spiritual Aspects Of Money **Chapter 20** - Do It Daily

PERSONAL FINANCE IS 80% BEHAVIOR AND ONLY 20% KNOWLEDGE

The most proven method to ensure you implement the principles found in Dave's book is Financial Peace University.

Member Resource Center
Complete Your FPU Experience Online!

visit www.daveramsey.com/fpumember

YOUR FPU CLASS CODE :

116688

Ask your FPU Class Coordinator for your Class Code. You will need your Class Code to access the Member Resouce Center. If you are not in a class, please visit us online at www.daveramsey.com/fpumember to get your Class Code.

You'll love the many benefits of using the Member Resource Center!

1. Register for your lifetime FPU Membership.
2. The easiest way to complete your homework online.
3. Access to a wide range of online financial tools and resources.
4. Take advantage of special offers and important updates.
5. Qualify to be entered into drawings for special prizes.

To start using this FREE resource today visit:

www.daveramsey.com/fpumember

Dave Ramsey's Financial Peace University

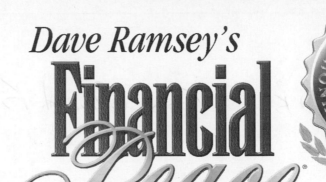

Super Savers

Travis Foster

"If you do the things you need when you need to do them, then someday you can do the things you want to do when you want to do them."

Zig Ziglar

☑ **Notes:**

GOK — God Only Knows

Save, Save, Save, Please Save!

- Saving must become a _PRIORITY_.

- You must pay yourself _FIRST_.

- Give, save, then pay _BILLS_.

- Saving money is about _EMOTION_ and _CONTENTMENT_.

- Building wealth is not evil or wrong. Money is _AMORAL_.

> *"For the love of money is a root of all kinds of evil."*
>
> *1 Timothy 6:10 (NIV)*

- Larry Burkett, famous Christian author, says, "The only difference in saving and hoarding is _ATTITUDE_."

You should save for three basic reasons:

   1. _EMERGENCY_ _FUND_

   2. _Purchases_

   3. _WEALTH_ _BUILDING_

- You must start _NOW_ !!!!

Ben & Arthur: Both save at 12%, both save $2,000 per year.
Ben starts at age 19 and stops at age 26. Arthur starts at age 27 and stops at age 65...

AGE	BEN INVESTS		ARTHUR INVESTS	
19	2,000	2,240	0	0
20	2,000	4,749	0	0
21	2,000	7,558	0	0
22	2,000	10,706	0	0
23	2,000	14,230	0	0
24	2,000	18,178	0	0
25	2,000	22,599	0	0
26	2,000	27,551	0	0
27	0	30,857	2,000	2,240
28	0	34,560	2,000	4,749
29	0	38,708	2,000	7,558
30	0	43,352	2,000	10,706
31	0	48,554	2,000	14,230
32	0	54,381	2,000	18,178
33	0	60,907	2,000	22,599
34	0	68,216	2,000	27,551
35	0	76,802	2,000	33,097
36	0	85,570	2,000	39,309
37	0	95,383	2,000	46,266
38	0	107,339	2,000	54,058
39	0	120,220	2,000	62,785
40	0	134,646	2,000	72,559
41	0	150,804	2,000	83,506
42	0	168,900	2,000	95,767
43	0	189,168	2,000	109,499
44	0	211,869	2,000	124,879
45	0	237,293	2,000	142,104
46	0	265,768	2,000	161,396
47	0	297,660	2,000	183,004
48	0	333,379	2,000	207,204
49	0	373,385	2,000	234,308
50	0	418,191	2,000	264,665
51	0	468,374	2,000	298,665
52	0	524,579	2,000	336,745
53	0	587,528	2,000	379,394
54	0	658,032	2,000	427,161
55	0	736,995	2,000	480,660
56	0	825,435	2,000	540,579
57	0	924,487	2,000	607,688
		1,035,425	2,000	682,851
		1,159,676	2,000	767,033
		1,298,837	2,000	861,317
		1,454,698	2,000	966,915
62	0	1,629,261	2,000	1,085,185
63	0	1,824,773	2,000	1,217,647
64	0	2,043,746	2,000	1,366,005
65	0	2,288,996	2,000	1,532,166

$2,288,996
With only a
$16,000
Investment

$1,532,166
Arthur NEVER
caught up!

Emergency Fund

- ___UNEXPECTED___ events do occur - expect it !!!

> "And let them gather all the food of those good years that are coming, and store up grain under the authority of Pharaoh, and let them keep food in the cities. Then that food shall be as a reserve for the land for the seven years of famine which shall be in the land of Egypt, that the land may not perish during the famine."
>
> Genesis 41:35-36 (NKJV)

In our lives, we all go through 'times of famine'. Whether it's a layoff, lengthy illness, large financial loss, etc., we need to be prepared and save up while we can. It will allow us to better cope during tough times and, in some cases, to survive.

- Step One, a beginner emergency fund is ___$1,000⁰⁰___ in the bank. ($500 if your household income is below $20,000 per year)

- Most financial planners and CPAs recommend you should have ___3-6___ months of your expenses in easily accessible savings — cash. ___10-15K___

- A great place to keep your emergency fund is in a ___Money Market___ account from a mutual fund company.

- Your emergency fund is ___PROTECTION___ for you and your investment programs and is not a big ___EARNER___.

- Do not ___TOUCH___ this fund for purchases.

- The Emergency Fund is the ___FIRST___ thing for which you save.

Purchases

- Instead of ___Borrowing___ to purchase, pay cash by using a ___Sinking___ fund approach.

- If you borrow to purchase a $ __4000°°__ dining room suite, most furniture stores sell their financing contracts to finance companies; this means you will have borrowed at __24__ % with payments of $ __211__ per month for __24__ months. So you will pay a total of $ __5075__ , plus insurance, for that suite.

- But if you save the same $ __211__ per month for only __18__ months at __0__ %, you will be able to pay cash.

- When you pay cash you can <u>always negotiate</u> a discount, so you will be able to buy it even earlier.

- Save for a $5,000 car by putting $ __500__ per month in the cookie jar for only 10 months!

- Since we have pledged to borrow no more, this is the only way to make a purchase.

"One definition of maturity is "delaying <u>pleasure</u>."

Dave Ramsey

Super Savers

Wealth Building

Retirement Planning, College Funding, Etc.

> *"In the house of the wise are stores of choice food and oil, but a foolish man devours all he has."*
>
> *Proverbs 21:20 (NIV)*

- _DISCIPLINE_ is a key ingredient.

- You must be _Consistent_ over _Time_.

> *"A faithful man will abound with blessings, but he who hastens to be rich will not go unpunished."*
>
> *Proverbs 28:20 (NKJV)*

Someone who is faithful about saving a little money every month over a lifetime will build wealth. Too many people try a get-rich-quick scheme and lose their money. Save consistently over time.

- _40_ years of saving $_100_ per month, every month, at _12_ % will build to $_1,176,470.00_.

- Pre-Authorized Checking (PACs) withdrawals are a good way to build in _DISCIPLINE_.

• Compound interest is a mathematical _EXPLOSION_.

> *"...If riches increase, do not set your heart on them."*
>
> *Psalms 62:10 (NKJV)*

• Rate of return or _INTEREST_ rate is important.

> *"Make all you can, save all you can, give all you can."*
>
> *John Wesley*

Super Savers

✓ Investments

$1,000 one-time investment, no withdrawal
Age 25 to Age 65 (40 years)

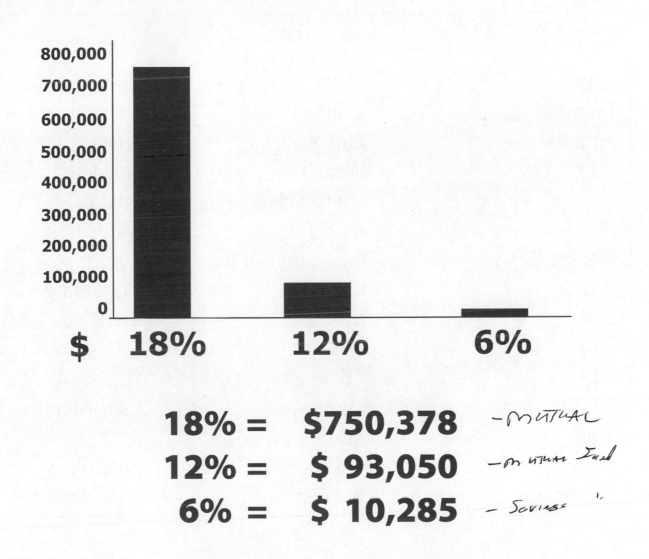

	18%	12%	6%

18% = $750,378   —MUTUAL

12% = $ 93,050   —mutual fund

6% = $ 10,285   — Savings "

Discussion Questions

1. Why have we quit saving in modern America?

2. What are some of the emotional benefits of saving?

3. What is the process for you to begin saving?

Answer Key (left to right)		
Priority	First	Bills
Emotion	Contentment	Amoral
Attitude	Emergency	Fund
Purchases	Wealth	Building
Now	Unexpected	$1,000
3	6	Money
Market	Protection	Earner
Touch	First	Borrowing
Sinking	4,000	24
211	24	5,075
211	18	0
$500	Discipline	Consistent
Time	40	100
12%	1,176,477	Discipline
Explosion	Interest	

Super Savers

Accountability Check-Up

Super Savers

I.   Get to know one another (1-2 minutes per family).
    A. Discuss why you came to the program.
    B. What do you hope to get out of this program?
    C. BE HONEST, OPEN AND REAL WITH EACH OTHER!

II.   Review - Discussion Questions AT THE END OF LESSON #1.

III. Review pages 14-17: It's Time To Begin, Baby Steps, and the Buddy System.

IV.   ACCOUNTABILITY & APPLICATION REVIEW: Each person or couple should comment about these questions.
    A. I will or have started making SAVINGS a priority because …   (everyone share reasons with group).
    B. (Yes/No) I balance my checkbook online or within 72 hours of receiving my bank statement. Why or why not? Why is it important to balance (reconcile) your account?
    C. In the past my emergency fund came from … (List source you used to come up with money when needed for emergencies. For example: credit cards, loans, family, etc.) Why did you turn to this source for money? How did it make you feel?
    D. What do you consider to be an "emergency" that would justify tapping into your emergency fund? (If married, does your spouse agree with you about this?)
    E. I will write down and set small bite-size goals to achieve during this 13-week program (with my spouse, if married) this week.

V.   Go home and write down on paper (with your spouse, if married) what you consider to be a real emergency, so that if you have to touch your emergency fund, you can feel good about it and not rob it over some meaningless, false justification.

VI.   Be prepared to show your BASIC QUICKIE BUDGET next week.

* Be sure to register for your Lifetime FPU Membership the easy way, online.
* You can also complete your homework online, and get great financial tools and resources for this week's lesson.
    * Log in using your class code on page 22.

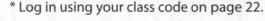

* If you complete the assignments in the Member Resource Center for all FPU lessons, you will be entered into drawings for special prizes!
Note: The content, tools and prizes are subject to change (i.e. get better).

provides HOPE and offers education that will enable you to:
- Identify your situation and goals for the future
- Gain control
- Create a plan for short and long term financial security

We can help you achieve your finacial goals by offering the following one-on-one consultations to choose from:

Tune-Up - specifically designed for the financially healthy who want an unbiased review and recommendations of their financial plan.

Small Business - designed to assist small business owners (with three or more employees) in assessing their present financial situation and make recommendations to achieve company goals.

Challenge Session - designed for families facing creditors, bankruptcy, foreclosure and stress that seems never-ending. The sessions can provide HOPE and the tools to work through even the worst financial situations (includes Financial Peace University).

Phone Counseling - provided only for clients more than one hour away from our office.

1-888-22PEACE

All counseling at Dave's Office is offered for a fee and includes a 30-day guarantee.
You must attend counseling with your spouse, if you are married.

Dave Ramsey's
Financial Peace University
Cash Flow Planning

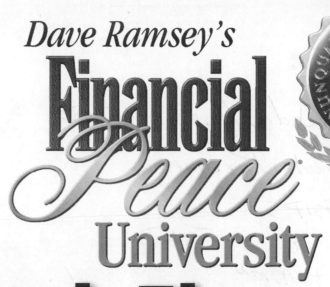

Travis Foster

"For which of you, intending to build a tower, does not sit down first and count the cost, whether he has enough to finish it- lest... all who see it begin to mock him, saying, 'This man began to build and was not able to finish.'"

Luke 14:28-30 (NKJV)

Birthday/Gifts - Fund

School Pictures

Trips

Xmas   Fund

Vacation

Wedding

New York

Furniture

Personal Property Tax

Blow $

Different Envs for Each Car.

Allowance / Commission

Hair Cut

Show Choir

Cash Flow Planning

Cash Flow Planning

- Money is __ACTIVE__.

- You must do a written __CASH__ __FLOW__ plan monthly.

> *"Be diligent to know the state of your flocks and attend to your herds."*
> *Proverbs 27:23 (NKJV)*

Many years ago, your wealth was measured by the amount of livestock you had instead of dollars. You had to tend to your herds and flocks every month to see that they were fed and didn't run away. Today you need to look over the dollars of personal finance every month to make sure they aren't dwindling away, too.

- You must also keep your __Check book__ balanced.

- Bounced checks are a sign of crisis __LIVING__ and sloppy, lazy money habits.

- Use __CARBON__ checks if necessary.

- If not managed and made to behave, the __ATM__ card and the __Debit__ card are certain to become budget busters. *use them as part of the GAME Plan. NOT on Impuls*

> *"Prepare your outside work, make it fit for yourself in the field; and afterward build your house."*
> *Proverbs 24:27 (NKJV)*

Reasons We DON'T Do a Cash Flow Plan

- Most people hate the word "budget" for four reasons:

    1) It has a ___BREAD___ and ___WATER___ connotation.

    2) It has been used to ___ABUSE___ you.

    3) They never had a budget that ___Worked___.

    4) Paralysis from ___FEAR___ of what we will find.

- Cash Flow Plans do not work because you:

    1) ___Leave___ things ___out___.

    2) Over ___Complicate___ your plan.

    3) Don't actually ___DO___ it.

    4) Don't actually ___Live___ on it.

-Food
-Shelter
-Clothing
-Transportation

Cash Flow Planning

Reasons We SHOULD Do a Cash Flow Plan

- A written plan removes the "management by ___CRISIS___" from your finances.

> *"The plans of the diligent lead surely to plenty, But those of everyone who is hasty, surely to poverty."*
>
> *Proverbs 21:5 (NKJV)*

- Managed money goes ___FARTHER___.

> *"People don't plan to fail, they fail to plan."*
>
> *Anonymous*

> *"Commit your works to the Lord, and your thoughts will be established."*
>
> *Proverbs 16:3 (NKJV)*

- A written plan, if actually lived and agreed on, will remove many of the ___Money___ ___fights___ from your marriage.

- A written plan, if actually lived and agreed on, will remove much of the ___Guilt___, ___Shame___, and ___fear___ that may now be a part of buying necessities such as food or clothing.

- A written plan, if actually lived and agreed on, will remove many of the _Bounced_ _Checks_ from your life, consequently removing a lot of _Stress_.

> "Worry often gives a small thing a big shadow."
>
> Swedish Proverb

> "May He give you the desire of your heart and make all your plans succeed."
>
> Psalms 20:4 (NIV)

- A written plan, if actually lived and agreed on, will show if you are _over_ _Spending_ on a certain area.

> "When you're afraid, keep your mind on what you have to do. And if you have been thoroughly prepared, you will not be afraid."
>
> Dale Carnegie

> "'Woe to the rebellious children,' says the Lord, 'Who take counsel, but not of Me, And who devise plans, but not of My spirit, That they may add to sin.'"
>
> Isaiah 30:1 (NKJV)

The easiest and most powerful plan is a _Zero_-based plan using the _Envelope_ system.

Cash Flow Planning

"Baby Steps"

There is a process to getting out of the mess that we created without feeling overwhelmed. Getting out of debt will not happen overnight; it takes time. Here are the Baby Steps to begin the process:

Step 1: $1,000.00 in an Emergency Fund
                  ($500.00 if income under $20,000 per year)

Step 2:   Pay off <u>all debt except</u> the house utilizing the Debt Snowball
                  (found in the Dumping Debt lesson)

Step 3:   Three to six months expenses in savings

Step 4:   Invest 15% of household income into Roth IRAs and pre-tax retirement

Step 5:   College funding

Step 6:   Pay off home early

Step 7:   Build wealth!
                  (Mutual funds, Real Estate)

cash flow planning

How to Balance Your Checkbook

- Keep your checkbook register current by subtracting both checks and withdrawals and adding deposits as they're made to keep your checkbook balanced correctly.

- Balance your checking account within 72 hours of receiving your bank statement or online once a month to make sure there aren't any mistakes.

- What do I need to balance my checkbook?
  1. Your checkbook register
  2. Your last bank statement
  3. A reconciliation sheet (located on the back of most statements)

- Where do I start?   Checkbook vs. Bank Statement

  Start by putting check marks in your checkbook for each of the checks and deposits included in your bank statement. Make an entry in your checkbook for any bank service charges (or interest paid) made by the bank.

Checkbook Register						
Check Number	Date	Fee	Transaction Description	Payment	Deposit	Balance
						$564.46
5671	8/12	X	One Stop Grocery	57.40		507.06
5672	8/14		Electric Company	101.00		406.06
	8/14		Paycheck		700.00	1106.06
5673	8/16		Telephone Company	50.00		1056.06
5674	8/19		One Stop Grocery	66.00		990.06
		X	Bank Service Charge	2.50		987.56

Cash Flow Planning

Bank Balance Example

- On the Reconciliation sheet, list any checks and/or withdrawals or other deductions that are in your checkbook that are not on your bank statement and total the list.

- On the Reconciliation sheet, list any deposits that are in your checkbook but are not included on your bank statement. Total the list.

- Beginning with the ending balance from your bank statement, subtract the total withdrawals and add the total deposits that were not on your statement.

- Compare with your checkbook balance. If they don't agree, double check your lists and re-add your checkbook entries until you find the difference.

List the balance from your bank statement $ 504.56

List the checks from your checkbook that aren't on your statement

The Electric Company	5672	8/14	101.00
Telephone Company	5673	8/16	50.00
One Stop Grocery	5674	8/19	66.00

TOTAL $ (217.00)   (-) $ 217.00

List the deposit amounts in your checkbook that aren't on your statement

Paycheck	8/14		700.00

TOTAL $ (700.00) (+) $ 700.00

This should be your checkbook balance $ (987.56)

Financial Management Forms

Welcome to the wonderful world of "cash flow management." Filling out these few forms and following your new plan will change your financial future. The first time you fill out the forms it will be tough and will take a while. But each time you come back for another look, you will get faster and the forms will be easier, so don't get discouraged. The length and the amount of detail I am taking you through may seem overwhelming. However, I have found that if you don't have the detail as a track to run on you leave something out. Guess what that does? If you leave items out that you are actually spending, you will crash your plan and then you will have an excuse to quit, so just bear down and do all the forms completely, one time.

After you have filled out the whole set once, you only need to do Sheet 7 or Sheet 8 (whichever is applicable) once per month which should take about 30 minutes. Do Sheet 5 over once per month, but since you will see only minor changes from one month to the next, you should only need about one hour per month to update. Then update the entire pack once per year or when any large positive or negative financial event occurs (Aunt Ethel leaves you $10,000 in her will).

Once you have made it through this planning process the first time you should be able to manage your finances in 30 minutes per month plus what it takes to write checks and balance your checkbook. Go for it!!

P. S. Be sure you keep your promises on Sheet 1 and share that completed sheet with your spouse, if married.

Cash Flow Planning

Major Components of a Healthy Financial Plan

Sheet 1

	Action Needed	Action Date
Written Cash Flow Plan	_____	_____
Will and/or Estate Plan	_____	_____
Debt Reduction Plan	_____	_____
Tax Reduction Plan	_____	_____
Emergency Funding	_____	_____
Retirement Funding	_____	_____
College Funding	_____	_____
Charitable Giving	_____	_____
Teach My Children	_____	_____
Life Insurance	_____	_____
Health Insurance	_____	_____
Disability Insurance	_____	_____
Auto Insurance	_____	_____
Homeowners Insurance	_____	_____

cash flow planning

I (We) _____, (a) responsible adult(s), do hereby promise to take the above stated actions by the above stated dates to financially secure the well-being of my (our) family and myself (ourselves).

Signed:_____ Date:_____
              (Nerd)

Signed:_____ Date:_____
              (Free spirit)

Consumer Equity Sheet

ITEM / DESCRIBE	VALUE	- DEBT	= EQUITY
Real Estate _____	$90,000	$70,000	$20,000
Real Estate _____			
Car _____			
Car _____	$7,000	$10,000	-$3,000
Cash On Hand			
Checking Account			
Checking Account			
Savings Account	$1,000	0	$1,000
Savings Account			
Money Market Account			
Mutual Funds			
Retirement Plan	$7,000	0	$7,000
Cash Value (Insurance)			
Household Items			
Jewelry			
Antiques			
Boat			
Unsecured Debt (Neg)	0	$7,000	-$7,000
Credit Card Debt (Neg)			
Other _____			
Other _____			
Other _____			
TOTAL	$105,000	$87,000	$18,000

Cash Flow Planning

cash flow planning

Consumer Equity Sheet

Sheet 2

ITEM / DESCRIBE	VALUE	- DEBT	= EQUITY
Real Estate _____	_____	_____	_____
Real Estate _____	_____	_____	_____
Car _____	_____	_____	_____
Car _____	_____	_____	_____
Cash On Hand	_____	_____	_____
Checking Account	_____	_____	_____
Checking Account	_____	_____	_____
Savings Account	_____	_____	_____
Savings Account	_____	_____	_____
Money Market Account	_____	_____	_____
Mutual Funds	_____	_____	_____
Retirement Plan	_____	_____	_____
Cash Value (Insurance)	_____	_____	_____
Household Items	_____	_____	_____
Jewelry	_____	_____	_____
Antiques	_____	_____	_____
Boat	_____	_____	_____
Unsecured Debt (Neg)	_____	_____	_____
Credit Card Debt (Neg)	_____	_____	_____
Other _____	_____	_____	_____
Other _____	_____	_____	_____
Other _____	_____	_____	_____
TOTAL	_____	_____	_____

cash flow planning

Income Sources

Sheet 3

SOURCE	AMOUNT	PERIOD/DESCRIBE
Salary 1 — *Take Home Pay*	$1700	1st & 15th - $850
Salary 2	$1300	2 WEEKS - $650
Salary 3		
Bonus		
Self-Employment		
Interest Income		
Dividend Income		
Royalty Income		
Rents		
Notes		
Alimony		
Child Support		
AFDC		
Unemployment		
Social Security		
Pension		
Annuity		
Disability Income		
Cash Gifts		
Trust Fund		
Other _____		
Other _____		
Other _____		
TOTAL	$3000	

 **Income Sources**

SOURCE	AMOUNT	PERIOD/DESCRIBE
Salary 1	_____	_____
Salary 2	_____	_____
Salary 3	_____	_____
Bonus	_____	_____
Self-Employment	_____	_____
Interest Income	_____	_____
Dividend Income	_____	_____
Royalty Income	_____	_____
Rents	_____	_____
Notes	_____	_____
Alimony	_____	_____
Child Support	_____	_____
AFDC	_____	_____
Unemployment	_____	_____
Social Security	_____	_____
Pension	_____	_____
Annuity	_____	_____
Disability Income	_____	_____
Cash Gifts	_____	_____
Trust Fund	_____	_____
Other _____	_____	_____
Other _____	_____	_____
Other _____	_____	_____
TOTAL	_____	

cash flow planning

Lump Sum Payment Planning

Sheet 4

Payments you make on a NON-monthly basis can be budget busters if not planned for, so we are converting them to a monthly basis for you to use on Sheet 5 where you will set money aside monthly to avoid strain or borrowing when these events occur. If an item here is already paid monthly, enter NA. If you make a payment quarterly then annualize it for this sheet.

ITEM NEEDED	ANNUAL AMOUNT		MONTHLY AMOUNT
Real Estate Taxes		/ 12 =	
Homeowners Insurance		/ 12 =	
Home Repairs	$600	/ 12 =	$50
Replace Furniture		/ 12 =	
Medical Bills		/ 12 =	
Health Insurance		/ 12 =	
Life Insurance		/ 12 =	
Disability Insurance		/ 12 =	
Car Insurance		/ 12 =	
Car Repair/Tags		/ 12 =	
Replace Car		/ 12 =	
Clothing		/ 12 =	
Tuition		/ 12 =	
Bank Note		/ 12 =	
IRS (Self-Employed)	$1800	/ 12 =	$150
Vacation	$1200	/ 12 =	$100
Gifts (inc. Christmas)		/ 12 =	
Other _____		/ 12 =	

Cash Flow Planning

Lump Sum Payment Planning

Payments you make on a NON-monthly basis can be budget busters if not planned for, so we are converting them to a monthly basis for you to use on Sheet 5 where you will set money aside monthly to avoid strain or borrowing when these events occur. If an item here is already paid monthly, enter NA. If you make a payment quarterly then annualize it for this sheet.

ITEM NEEDED	ANNUAL AMOUNT		MONTHLY AMOUNT
Real Estate Taxes	_____	/ 12 =	_____
Homeowners Insurance	_____	/ 12 =	_____
Home Repairs	_____	/ 12 =	_____
Replace Furniture	_____	/ 12 =	_____
Medical Bills	_____	/ 12 =	_____
Health Insurance	_____	/ 12 =	_____
Life Insurance	_____	/ 12 =	_____
Disability Insurance	_____	/ 12 =	_____
Car Insurance	_____	/ 12 =	_____
Car Repair/Tags	_____	/ 12 =	_____
Replace Car	_____	/ 12 =	_____
Clothing	_____	/ 12 =	_____
Tuition	_____	/ 12 =	_____
Bank Note	_____	/ 12 =	_____
IRS (Self-Employed)	_____	/ 12 =	_____
Vacation	_____	/ 12 =	_____
Gifts (inc. Christmas)	_____	/ 12 =	_____
Other _____	_____	/ 12 =	_____

cash flow planning

 **Notes:**

Cash Flow Planning

Instructions Sheet 5

Every dollar of your income should be allocated to some category on this sheet. Money "left over" should be put back into a category even if you make up a new category. You are making the spending decisions ahead of time here. Almost every category (except debt) should have some dollar amount in it. Example: If you do not plan to replace the furniture, when you do replace it, you will cause strain or borrowing, so go ahead and plan now by saving. I have actually had people tell me that they can do without clothing. Oh come ON!! Be careful in your zeal to make the numbers work that you don't substitute the urgent for the important.

Fill in the amount for each subcategory under "Subtotal" and then the total for each main category under "Total." As you go through your first month, fill in the "Actually Spent" column with your real expenses or the saving you did for that area. If there is a substantial difference in the plan versus the reality, something has to give. You will either have to adjust the amount allocated to that area up and another down, or you will have to better control your spending in that area.

"Percent (%) Take-Home Pay" is the percentage of take-home pay that category represents. For example, the percentage of your total take-home you spent on "Housing." We will then compare your percentages with those on Sheet 6 to determine if you need to consider adjusting your lifestyle.

An asterick (*) beside an item means you should use the "envelope system."

The Emergency Fund should get ALL the savings until three to six months of expenses have been saved.

Note: Savings should be increased as you get closer to being debt-free.

Hint: By saving early for Christmas and other gifts, you can get great buys and give better gifts for the same money.

- *You have three sets of "Monthly Cash Flow Plan" sheets located at the end of the thirteen lessons.*
- *Use these forms as your zero-based budget forms which will be checked every few weeks by your group leaders.*
- *Make enough copies to do this for a one-year period in order to help you develop proper financial management habits.*

Monthly Cash Flow Plan

cash flow planning

Budgeted Item	Sub Total	TOTAL	Actually Spent	% of Take Home Pay
CHARITABLE GIFTS		$300		10%
SAVING				
Emergency Fund	$50			
Retirement Fund				
College Fund		$50		
HOUSING				
First Mortgage	$725			
Second Mortgage				
Real Estate Taxes				
Homeowners Ins.				
Repairs or Mn. Fee				
Replace Furniture	$50			
Other		$775		
UTILITIES				
Electricity	$100			
Water	$50			
Gas	$50			
Phone	$50			
Trash				
Cable		$250		
***FOOD**				
*Grocery	$600			
*Restaurants	$100	$700		
TRANSPORTATION				
Car Payment				
Car Payment				
*Gas and Oil				
*Repairs and Tires				
Car Insurance				
License and Taxes				
Car Replacement				
PAGE 1 TOTAL		$2075		

Monthly Cash Flow Plan

Sheet 5

Budgeted Item	Sub Total	TOTAL	Actually Spent	% of Take Home Pay
CHARITABLE GIFTS		_____	_____	_____
SAVING				
Emergency Fund	_____		_____	
Retirement Fund	_____		_____	
College Fund	_____		_____	_____
HOUSING				
First Mortgage	_____		_____	
Second Mortgage	_____		_____	
Real Estate Taxes	_____		_____	
Homeowners Ins.	_____		_____	
Repairs or Mn. Fee	_____		_____	
Replace Furniture	_____		_____	
Other _____	_____	_____	_____	_____
UTILITIES				
Electricity	_____		_____	
Water	_____		_____	
Gas	_____		_____	
Phone	_____		_____	
Trash	_____		_____	
Cable	_____	_____	_____	_____
***FOOD**				
*Grocery	_____		_____	
*Restaurants	_____	_____	_____	_____
TRANSPORTATION				
Car Payment	_____		_____	
Car Payment	_____		_____	
*Gas and Oil	_____		_____	
*Repairs and Tires	_____		_____	
Car Insurance	_____		_____	
License and Taxes	_____		_____	
Car Replacement	_____	_____	_____	_____
PAGE 1 TOTAL		_____	_____	

Monthly Cash Flow Plan

Sheet 5 Continued

Budgeted Item	Sub Total	TOTAL	Actually Spent	% of Take Home Pay
*CLOTHING				
*Children	$100			
*Adults				
*Cleaning/Laundry		$100		
MEDICAL/HEALTH				
Disability Insurance	$100			
Health Insurance				
Doctor Bills	$50			
Dentist	$20			
Optometrist				
Drugs		$170		
PERSONAL				
Life Insurance	$50			
Child Care	$30			
*Baby Sitter				
*Toiletries				
*Cosmetics				
*Hair Care				
Education/Adult				
School Tuition				
School Supplies				
Child Support				
Alimony				
Subscriptions				
Organization Dues	$25			
Gifts (incl. Christmas)				
Miscellaneous	$50			
*BLOW $$	$100	$255		
PAGE 2 TOTAL		$525		

Cash Flow Planning

cash flow planning

 **Monthly Cash Flow Plan**

Sheet 5 Continued

Budgeted Item	Sub Total	TOTAL	Actually Spent	% of Take Home Pay
*CLOTHING				
*Children	_____		_____	
*Adults	_____		_____	
*Cleaning/Laundry	_____	_____	_____	_____
MEDICAL/HEALTH				
Disability Insurance	_____		_____	
Health Insurance	_____		_____	
Doctor Bills	_____		_____	
Dentist	_____		_____	
Optometrist	_____		_____	
Drugs	_____	_____	_____	_____
PERSONAL				
Life Insurance	_____		_____	
Child Care	_____		_____	
*Baby Sitter	_____		_____	
*Toiletries	_____		_____	
*Cosmetics	_____		_____	
*Hair Care	_____		_____	
Education/Adult	_____		_____	
School Tuition	_____		_____	
School Supplies	_____		_____	
Child Support	_____		_____	
Alimony	_____		_____	
Subscriptions	_____		_____	
Organization Dues	_____		_____	
Gifts (incl. Christmas)	_____		_____	
Miscellaneous	_____		_____	
*BLOW $$	_____	_____	_____	_____
PAGE 2 TOTAL		_____		

Monthly Cash Flow Plan

Budgeted Item	Sub Total	TOTAL	Actually Spent	% of Take Home Pay
RECREATION				
*Entertainment	$50			
Vacation	$25	$75		
DEBTS (Hopefully -0-)				
Visa 1	$100			
Visa 2				
Master Card 1	$75			
Master Card 2				
American Express	$50			
Discover Card				
Gas Card 1				
Gas Card 2				
Dept. Store Card 1				
Dept. Store Card 2				
Finance Co. 1				
Finance Co. 2				
Credit Line				
Student Loan 1	$100			
Student Loan 2				
Other _____				
Other _____				
Other _____				
Other _____				
Other _____		$325		
PAGE 3 TOTAL		$400		
PAGE 2 TOTAL		$525		
PAGE 1 TOTAL		$2075		
GRAND TOTAL		$3000		
TOTAL HOUSEHOLD INCOME		$3000		
		ZERO		

cash flow planning

Monthly Cash Flow Plan

Sheet 5 Continued

Budgeted Item	Sub Total	TOTAL	Actually Spent	% of Take Home Pay
RECREATION				
*Entertainment	_____		_____	
Vacation	_____	_____	_____	_____
DEBTS (Hopefully -0-)				
Visa 1	_____		_____	
Visa 2	_____		_____	
Master Card 1	_____		_____	
Master Card 2	_____		_____	
American Express	_____		_____	
Discover Card	_____		_____	
Gas Card 1	_____		_____	
Gas Card 2	_____		_____	
Dept. Store Card 1	_____		_____	
Dept. Store Card 2	_____		_____	
Finance Co. 1	_____		_____	
Finance Co. 2	_____		_____	
Credit Line	_____		_____	
Student Loan 1	_____		_____	
Student Loan 2	_____		_____	
Other _____	_____		_____	
Other _____	_____		_____	
Other _____	_____		_____	
Other _____	_____		_____	
Other _____	_____		_____	_____

PAGE 3 TOTAL _____ _____

PAGE 2 TOTAL _____ _____

PAGE 1 TOTAL _____ _____

GRAND TOTAL _____ _____

TOTAL HOUSEHOLD INCOME _____

ZERO

cash flow planning

✓ Recommended Percentages

I have used a compilation of several sources and my own experience to derive the suggested percentage guidelines. However, these are only recommended percentages and will change dramatically if you have a very high or very low income. For instance, if you have a very low income, your necessities percentages will be high. If you have a high income your necessities will be a lower percentage of income and hopefully savings (not debt) will be higher than recommended.

ITEM	ACTUAL %	RECOMMENDED %
CHARITABLE GIFTS	_____	10 - 15%
SAVING	_____	5 - 10%
HOUSING	_____	25 - 35%
UTILITIES	_____	5 - 10%
FOOD	_____	5 - 15%
TRANSPORTATION	_____	10 - 15%
CLOTHING	_____	2 - 7%
MEDICAL/HEALTH	_____	5 - 10%
PERSONAL	_____	5 - 10%
RECREATION	_____	5 - 10%
DEBTS	_____	5 - 10%

Cash Flow Planning

 **Instructions Sheet 7**

This sheet is where all your work thus far starts giving you some peace. You will implement Sheet 5 information from theory into your life by using Sheet 7. Note: If you have an irregular income, like self-employment or commissions, you should use Sheet 8, after reviewing Sheet 7.

There are four columns to distribute as many as four different incomes within one month. Each column is one pay period. If you are a one-income household and you get paid two times per month then you will only use two columns. If both of you work and one is paid weekly and the other every two weeks, add the two paychecks together on the weeks you both get a paycheck, while just listing the one paycheck on the other two. Date the pay period columns, then enter the income for that period. As you allocate your paycheck to an Item, put the remaining total balance to the right of the slash. Income for period 3-1 in our example is $1,000 and we are allocating $100 to Charitable Giving leaving $900 to the right of the slash in that same column. Some bills will come out of each pay period and some only on selected pay periods. As an example, you may take "Car Gas" out of every paycheck, but pay the electric bill from period 2. You already pay some bills or payments out of designated checks, only now you pay all things from designated checks.

The whole point to this sheet, which is the culmination of all your monthly planning, is to allocate or "spend" your whole paycheck before you get paid. I don't care where you allocate your money, but allocate all of it before you get your check. Now all the tense, crisis-like symptoms have been removed because you planned. No more management by crisis or impulse. Those who tend to be impulsive should just allocate more to the "Blow" category. At least you are now doing it on purpose and not by default. The last blank that you make an entry in should have a zero to the right of the slash, showing you have allocated your whole check.

An asterick (*) beside an item means you should use the "envelope system."

Emergency Fund gets ALL the savings until three to six months of expenses have been saved.

```
SAMPLE ALLOCATED SPENDING PLAN

        PAY PERIOD:      3-1      _____    _____    _____
ITEM
INCOME                   1,000    _____    _____    _____
CHARITABLE GIFTS         100/900   __/__      __/__      __/__
SAVING
    Emergency Fund(1)    50/850    __/__      __/__      __/__
    Retirement Fund      __/__     __/__      __/__      __/__
    College Fund         __/__     __/__      __/__      __/__
HOUSING
    First Mortgage       725/125   __/__      __/__      __/__
```

Allocated Spending Plan

cash flow planning

PAY PERIOD:	8/1	8/8	8/15	8/22
ITEM:				
INCOME	$650	$850	$1500	0
CHARITABLE	75 / 575	/	/	/
SAVING				
Emergency Fund	50 / 525	/	/	/
Retirement Fund	/	/	/	/
College Fund	/	/	/	/
HOUSING				
First Mortgage	/	750 / 100	/	/
Second Mortgage	/	/	/	/
Real Estate Taxes	/	/	/	/
Homeowners Ins.	/	/	/	/
Repairs or Mn. Fees	/	/	/	/
Replace Furniture	50 / 475	/	/	/
Other	/	/	/	/
UTILITIES				
Electricity	100 / 375	/	/	/
Water	50 / 325	/	/	/
Gas	/	50 / 50	/	/
Phone	/	25 / 25	/	/
Trash	/	/	/	/
Cable	/	25 / 0	/	/
***FOOD**				
*Grocery	300 / 25	/	/	/
*Restaurants	25 / 0	/	/	/

Cash Flow Planning

Allocated Spending Plan

Sheet 7

PAY PERIOD: _____ _____ _____ _____

cash flow planning

ITEM:
INCOME   ___/___   ___/___   ___/___   ___/___
CHARITABLE ___/___   ___/___   ___/___   ___/___
SAVING

    Emergency Fund   ___/___   ___/___   ___/___   ___/___
    Retirement Fund ___/___   ___/___   ___/___   ___/___
    College Fund   ___/___   ___/___   ___/___   ___/___

HOUSING

    First Mortgage   ___/___   ___/___   ___/___   ___/___
    Second Mortgage   ___/___   ___/___   ___/___   ___/___
    Real Estate Taxes   ___/___   ___/___   ___/___   ___/___
    Homeowners Ins.   ___/___   ___/___   ___/___   ___/___
    Repairs or Mn. Fees ___/___   ___/___   ___/___   ___/___
    Replace Furniture   ___/___   ___/___   ___/___   ___/___
    Other _____   ___/___   ___/___   ___/___   ___/___

UTILITIES

    Electricity   ___/___   ___/___   ___/___   ___/___
    Water   ___/___   ___/___   ___/___   ___/___
    Gas   ___/___   ___/___   ___/___   ___/___
    Phone   ___/___   ___/___   ___/___   ___/___
    Trash   ___/___   ___/___   ___/___   ___/___
    Cable   ___/___   ___/___   ___/___   ___/___

*FOOD

    *Grocery   ___/___   ___/___   ___/___   ___/___
    *Restaurants ___/___   ___/___   ___/___   ___/___

Allocated Spending Plan

Sheet 7 continued

TRANSPORTATION
Car Payment _____/_____ _____/_____   _____/_____ _____/_____
Car Payment _____/_____ _____/_____   _____/_____ _____/_____
*Gas and Oil _____/_____ _____/_____   _____/_____ _____/_____
*Repairs and Tires _____/_____ _____/_____   _____/_____ _____/_____
Car Insurance _____/_____ _____/_____   _____/_____ _____/_____
License and Taxes _____/_____ _____/_____   _____/_____ _____/_____
Car Replacement _____/_____ _____/_____   _____/_____ _____/_____

*CLOTHING
*Children _____/_____ _____/_____   _____/_____ _____/_____
*Adults _____/_____ _____/_____   _____/_____ _____/_____
*Cleaning/Laundry _____/_____ _____/_____   _____/_____ _____/_____

MEDICAL/HEALTH
Disability Insurance _____/_____ _____/_____   _____/_____ _____/_____
Health Insurance _____/_____ _____/_____   _____/_____ _____/_____
Doctor _____/_____ _____/_____   _____/_____ _____/_____
Dentist _____/_____ _____/_____   _____/_____ _____/_____
Optometrist _____/_____ _____/_____   _____/_____ _____/_____
Drugs _____/_____ _____/_____   _____/_____ _____/_____

PERSONAL
Life Insurance _____/_____ _____/_____   _____/_____ _____/_____
Child Care _____/_____ _____/_____   _____/_____ _____/_____
*Baby Sitter _____/_____ _____/_____   _____/_____ _____/_____
*Toiletries _____/_____ _____/_____   _____/_____ _____/_____
*Cosmetics _____/_____ _____/_____   _____/_____ _____/_____
*Hair Care _____/_____ _____/_____   _____/_____ _____/_____
Education/Adult _____/_____ _____/_____   _____/_____ _____/_____
School Tuition _____/_____ _____/_____   _____/_____ _____/_____
School Supplies _____/_____ _____/_____   _____/_____ _____/_____
Child Support _____/_____ _____/_____   _____/_____ _____/_____

Cash Flow Planning

Allocated Spending Plan

Sheet 7 continued

Alimony ___/___ ___/___   ___/___ ___/___
Subscriptions ___/___ ___/___   ___/___ ___/___
Organization Dues ___/___ ___/___   ___/___ ___/___
Gifts (inc.Christmas) ___/___ ___/___   ___/___ ___/___
Miscellaneous ___/___ ___/___   ___/___ ___/___
*BLOW $$ ___/___ ___/___   ___/___ ___/___

RECREATION

*Entertainment ___/___ ___/___   ___/___ ___/___
Vacation ___/___ ___/___   ___/___ ___/___

DEBTS (Hopefully -0-)

Visa 1 ___/___ ___/___   ___/___ ___/___
Visa 2 ___/___ ___/___   ___/___ ___/___
MasterCard 1 ___/___ ___/___   ___/___ ___/___
MasterCard 2 ___/___ ___/___   ___/___ ___/___
American Express ___/___ ___/___   ___/___ ___/___
Discover Card ___/___ ___/___   ___/___ ___/___
Gas Card 1 ___/___ ___/___   ___/___ ___/___
Gas Card 2 ___/___ ___/___   ___/___ ___/___
Dept. Store Card 1 ___/___ ___/___   ___/___ ___/___
Dept. Store Card 2 ___/___ ___/___   ___/___ ___/___
Finance Co. 1 ___/___ ___/___   ___/___ ___/___
Finance Co. 2 ___/___ ___/___   ___/___ ___/___
Credit Line ___/___ ___/___   ___/___ ___/___
Student Loan 1 ___/___ ___/___   ___/___ ___/___
Student Loan 2 ___/___ ___/___   ___/___ ___/___
Other _____ ___/___ ___/___   ___/___ ___/___
Other _____ ___/___ ___/___   ___/___ ___/___
Other _____ ___/___ ___/___   ___/___ ___/___
Other _____ ___/___ ___/___   ___/___ ___/___
Other _____ ___/___ ___/___   ___/___ ___/___

Irregular Income Planning

cash flow planning

Many of us have irregular incomes. If you are self-employed or work on commission or royalties, then planning your expenses is difficult since you cannot always predict your income. You should still do all the sheets except Sheet 7. Sheet 5 will tell you what you have to earn monthly to survive or prosper, and those real numbers are very good for goal setting.

What you must do is take the items on Sheet 5 and prioritize them by importance. I repeat: by importance, not urgency. You should ask yourself, "If I only have enough money to pay one thing, what would that be?" Then ask, "If I only have enough money to pay one more thing, what will that be?" Move this way through the list. Now be prepared to stand your ground because things have a way of seeming important when they are only urgent. Saving should be a high priority!

The third column, "Cumulative Amount," is the total of all amounts above that item. So, if you get a $2,000 check, you can see how far down your priority list you can go.

Item	Amount	Cumulative Amount
Penny's	$150	$150
Sears	$250	$400
1/4 Couch	$500	$900
Vacation - part	$200	$1100
Christmas - part	$400	$1500
Visa	$500	$2000

Irregular Income Planning

Many of us have irregular incomes. If you are self-employed or work on commission or royalties, then planning your expenses is difficult since you cannot always predict your income. You should still do all the sheets except Sheet 7. Sheet 5 will tell you what you have to earn monthly to survive or prosper, and those real numbers are very good for goal setting.

What you must do is take the items on Sheet 5 and prioritize them by importance. I repeat: by importance, not urgency. You should ask yourself, "If I only have enough money to pay one thing, what would that be?" Then ask, "If I only have enough money to pay one more thing, what will that be?" Move this way through the list. Now be prepared to stand your ground because things have a way of seeming important when they are only urgent. Saving should be a high priority!

The third column, "Cumulative Amount," is the total of all amounts above that item. So, if you get a $2,000 check, you can see how far down your priority list you can go.

Item	Amount	Cumulative Amount
_____	_____	_____
_____	_____	_____
_____	_____	_____
_____	_____	_____
_____	_____	_____
_____	_____	_____
_____	_____	_____
_____	_____	_____

Breakdown of Savings

After your emergency fund is fully funded, you can save for certain items like furniture, car replacement, home maintenance, or clothes, and your savings balance will grow. This sheet is designed to remind you that all of that money is committed to something, not just a Hawaiian vacation on impulse because you are now "rich." Keep up with your breakdown of savings monthly for one quarter at a time.

Item	Balance By Month		
	September	October	November
Emergency Fund (1) $1,000			
Emergency Fund (2) 3-6 months			
Retirement Fund			
College Fund			
Real Estate Taxes			
Homeowners Insurance			
Repairs or Mn. Fee			
Replace Furniture	$600	$650	$700
Car Insurance			
Car Replacement			
Disability Insurance			
Health Insurance			
Doctor			
Dentist	$500	$500	$500
Optometrist			
Life Insurance			
School Tuition			
School Supplies	$600	$700	$800
Gifts (incl. Christmas)	$500	$650	$800
Vacation			
Other _____			
Other _____			
TOTAL	$2,200	$2,500	$2,800

cash flow planning

Breakdown of Savings

Sheet 9

After your emergency fund is fully funded, you can save for certain items like furniture, car replacement, home maintenance, or clothes, and your savings balance will grow. This sheet is designed to remind you that all of that money is committed to something, not just a Hawaiian vacation on impulse because you are now "rich." Keep up with your breakdown of savings monthly for one quarter at a time.

Item	Balance By Month		
Emergency Fund (1) $1,000			
Emergency Fund (2) 3-6 months			
Retirement Fund			
College Fund			
Real Estate Taxes			
Homeowners Insurance			
Repairs or Mn. Fee			
Replace Furniture			
Car Insurance			
Car Replacement			
Disability Insurance			
Health Insurance			
Doctor			
Dentist			
Optometrist			
Life Insurance			
School Tuition			
School Supplies			
Gifts (incl. Christmas)			
Vacation			
Other _____			
Other _____			
TOTAL			

Emergency Fund (1) is your first $1,000 (or $500 if your income is less than $20,000). After completing your debt snowball, Emergency Fund (2) gets all the savings until three to six months of expenses have been saved.

Debt Snowball

List your debts in order from smallest to largest with the smallest payoff or balance first. Do not be concerned with interest rates or terms unless two debts have similar payoffs, then list the higher interest rate debt first. Paying the little debts off first shows you quick feedback, and you are more likely to stay with the plan.

Redo this sheet each time you pay off a debt so you can see how close you are getting to freedom. Keep the old sheets to wallpaper the bathroom in your new debt-free house. The "New Payment" is found by adding all the payments on the debts listed above that item to the payment you are working on, so you have compounding payments which will get you out of debt very quickly. "Payments Remaining" is the number of payments remaining on that debt when you get down the snowball to that item. Cumulative Payments is the total payments needed, including the snowball, to pay off that item. In other words, this is your running total for "Payments Remaining."

COUNT DOWN TO FREEDOM!!

Date:_____

Item	Total Payoff	Minimum Payment	New Payment	Payments Remaining	Cumulative Payments
Penny's	$150	$15	$0	0	Garage Sale
Sears	$250	$10	$25	11	11
Visa	$500	$75	$100	PD	11
M.C.	$1500	$90	$190	5	16
Car	$4000	$210	$400	4	20
Stu. Loans	$4000	$65	$465	6	26

TOTALLY Debt Free except the house!
    Finish Emergency Fund
    Fund Retirement/College
    Then Do House

cash flow planning

Debt Snowball

Sheet 10

List your debts in order from smallest to largest with the smallest payoff or balance first. Do not be concerned with interest rates or terms unless two debts have similar payoffs, then list the higher interest rate debt first. Paying the little debts off first shows you quick feedback, and you are more likely to stay with the plan.

Redo this sheet each time you pay off a debt so you can see how close you are getting to freedom. Keep the old sheets to wallpaper the bathroom in your new debt-free house. The "New Payment" is found by adding all the payments on the debts listed above that item to the payment you are working on, so you have compounding payments which will get you out of debt very quickly. "Payments Remaining" is the number of payments remaining on that debt when you get down the snowball to that item. Cumulative Payments is the total payments needed, including the snowball, to pay off that item. In other words, this is your running total for "Payments Remaining."

COUNT DOWN TO FREEDOM!!

Date:_____

Item	Total Payoff	Minimum Payment	New Payment	Payments Remaining	Cumulative Payments

Pro Rata Debts

Discover	$1,200	$150
Citibank Visa	300	45
MBNA Visa	200	25
Penny's	100	60
Sears	200	30
TOTAL	$2,000	$310

Income	$2,400
Necessity Expense	- 2,200
Disposable Income	$ 200

Can't increase income anytime soon

Pro Rata Plan

Sheet 11

ITEM	TOTAL PAYOFF	TOTAL /DEBT	= PERCENT	DISPOSABLE X INCOME	NEW = PAYMENTS
Discover	1,200	/ 2000	= .60	X 200	= 120
Citibank	300	/ 2000	= .15	X 200	= 30
MBNA	200	/ 2000	= .10	X 200	= 20
Penny's	100	/ 2000	= .05	X 200	= 10
Sears	200	/ 2000	= .10	X 200	= 20

Cash Flow Planning

cash flow planning

Pro Rata Debts

If you cannot pay your creditors what they request, you should treat them all fairly and the same. You should pay even the ones who are not jerks and pay everyone as much as you can. Many creditors will accept a written plan and cut special deals with you as long as you are communicating, maybe even over communicating, and sending them something. We have had clients use this even when sending only $2 and have survived for literally years.

Pro rata means their share or what percent of your total debt they represent. That will determine how much you send them. You should send the check with a budget and this sheet attached each month, even if the creditor says they will not accept it.

cash flow planning

ITEM	TOTAL PAYOFF	TOTAL /DEBT	= PERCENT	DISPOSABLE x INCOME	NEW = PAYMENTS
____ ____	/ ____	= . ____	X ____	= ____
____ ____	/ ____	= . ____	X ____	= ____
____ ____	/ ____	= . ____	X ____	= ____
____ ____	/ ____	= . ____	X ____	= ____
____ ____	/ ____	= . ____	X ____	= ____
____ ____	/ ____	= . ____	X ____	= ____
____ ____	/ ____	= . ____	X ____	= ____
____ ____	/ ____	= . ____	X ____	= ____
____ ____	/ ____	= . ____	X ____	= ____
____ ____	/ ____	= . ____	X ____	= ____
____ ____	/ ____	= . ____	X ____	= ____
____ ____	/ ____	= . ____	X ____	= ____
____ ____	/ ____	= . ____	X ____	= ____
____ ____	/ ____	= . ____	X ____	= ____
____ ____	/ ____	= . ____	X ____	= ____
____ ____	/ ____	= . ____	X ____	= ____

Pro Rata Plan Letter

Date: Feb. 22, 2006

From: Joe and Suzie Public
      123 Anystreet
      Anytown, ST 11111

To: Mega Credit Card Company
    999 Main Street
    Big City, ST 00000

Re: Joe and Suzie Public # 1234-5678-9012-9999

Dear Collection Manager:

Recently I lost my job, and my wife is employed in a clerical position. We have met with a financial counselor to assess our present situation.

We acknowledge our indebtedness to you of $6,000 and fully intend to pay you back in full. However, you are one of six creditors to whom we owe $42,968. We owe minimum payments of $782 each month. We are not able to meet these minimum payments at the present time, and we are not planning on going into further debt to meet these obligations.

We have put together a basic necessities cash flow plan based on our take-home pay of $2,340 per month (see the enclosed copy of cash flow plan). Since we have two small children and no disposable income currently to pay our creditors, we can not make a payment to you at the present time, but we do not intend to go bankrupt.

Consequently, we are asking for a moratorium on payments for the next 120 days. We will keep in close contact with you, and as soon as possible, we will begin making payments. If possible, we would like to request a reduction on interest during this time.

We are aware that this is an inconvenience to you, but we must meet the basic needs of our family first. We fully intend to pay our creditors all that we owe them. Please be patient with us. If you have any questions please contact us at 600-555-9876.

Thank you for your consideration of our present situation.

Sincerely,

Joe Public
Suzie Public

cash flow planning

Pro Rata Plan Letter

Date: _____

From: _____
 _____
 _____

To: Name of Creditor
 Address

Re: Card holder name and account number

Dear: (If you know a specific person or, when contacting them by phone, get name of area or office supervisor.)

Recently (I have had to..........................) Or (my husband had.......................) changed jobs and have met with a financial counselor to assess our present situation.

We acknowledge our indebtedness to you of $_____, and fully intend to pay you back in full. However, you are one of _____ creditors to whom we owe $_____. We owe minimum payments of $_____ each month. We are not able to meet these minimum payments at the present time, and we are not planning on going into further debt to meet these obligations.

We have put together a basic necessities cash flow plan based on our take-home pay of $_____ per month (enclose copy of cash flow plan). Since we have _____ small children and no (or limited) disposable income currently to pay our creditors, we (can or cannot) make a payment to you (of $_____) at the present time, but we do not intend to go bankrupt.

Consequently, we are asking for a moratorium on payments for the next _____(30, 60, 90, or 120) days. We will keep in close contact with you, and as soon as possible, we will begin making payments. If possible, we would like to request a reduction on interest during this time.

We are aware that this is an inconvenience to you, but we must meet the basic needs of our family first. We fully intend to pay our creditors all that we owe them. Please be patient with us. If you have any questions please contact us at _____ (phone number).

Thank you for your consideration of our present situation.

Sincerely,
(Signatures)

✓ Monthly Retirement Planning

In order to retire with some security, you must aim at something. Too many people use the READY-FIRE-AIM approach to retirement planning. Your assignment is to determine how much per month you should be saving at 12% interest in order to retire at 65 years old with what you need.

If we are saving at 12% and inflation is at 4%, then we are moving ahead of inflation at a net of 8% per year. If you invest your nest egg at retirement at 12% and want to break even with 4% inflation, you will be living on 8% income.

Step 1:
Annual Income (today) you wish to retire on: _____ $30,000 _____

divide by .08

(nest egg needed) equals: _____ $375,000 _____

Step 2:
To achieve that nest egg, you will save at 12% netting 8% after inflation. So, we will target that nest egg using 8%.

_____$375,000_____	X	_____.000436_____	=	_____$163.50_____
Nest Egg Needed		Factor		Monthly Savings Needed

8% Factors (select the one that matches your age)		
Age	**Years to Save**	**Factor**
25	40	.000286
30	35	.000436
35	30	.000671
40	25	.001051
45	20	.001698
50	15	.002890
55	10	.005466
60	5	.013610

Note: Be sure to try one or two examples if you wait 5 or 10 years to start.

cash flow planning

Monthly Retirement Planning

Sheet 12

In order to retire with some security, you must aim at something. Too many people use the READY-FIRE-AIM approach to retirement planning. Your assignment is to determine how much per month you should be saving at 12% interest in order to retire at 65 years old with what you need.

If we are saving at 12% and inflation is at 4%, then we are moving ahead of inflation at a net of 8% per year. If you invest your nest egg at retirement at 12% and want to break even with 4% inflation, you will be living on 8% income.

Step 1:
Annual Income (today) you wish to retire on: _____
divide by .08
(nest egg needed) equals: _____

Step 2:
To achieve that nest egg, you will save at 12% netting 8% after inflation. So, we will target that nest egg using 8%.

_____ X _____ = _____
Nest Egg Needed   Factor   Monthly Savings Needed

8% Factors (select the one that matches your age)		
Age	**Years to Save**	**Factor**
25	40	.000286
30	35	.000436
35	30	.000671
40	25	.001051
45	20	.001698
50	15	.002890
55	10	.005466
60	5	.013610

Note: Be sure to try one or two examples if you wait 5 or 10 years to start.

Please complete the first column of the Financial Snapshot immediately following Session #3.

You can also easily complete your Financial Snapshot online! Go to www.daveramsey.com/fpumember for more information!

See next page for sample

CLASS START DATE (MM/DD/YY)

CLASS LOCATION CODE

Dave Ramsey's
Financial Peace University

FIRST NAME

SPOUSE FIRST NAME

LAST NAME

COORDINATOR FIRST NAME

COORDINATOR LAST NAME

Complete information in column 1, session #3, session #3, based upon your current financial situation since you started applying the "Financial Peace" principles, even if you started applying them prior to taking this FPU class.

Areas to work on IMMEDIATELY	Session #3	Session #6	Session #9	Session #12
Have a budget that works?	○ Yes ○ No	○ Yes ○ No	○ Yes ○ No	○ Yes ○ No
Paying necessities before creditors?	○ Yes ○ No	○ Yes ○ No	○ Yes ○ No	○ Yes ○ No
Cut up all credit cards?	○ Yes ○ No	○ Yes ○ No	○ Yes ○ No	○ Yes ○ No
Living on envelope system?	○ Yes ○ No	○ Yes ○ No	○ Yes ○ No	○ Yes ○ No
How many envelopes?				
$1,000 in emergency fund?	○ Yes ○ No	○ Yes ○ No	○ Yes ○ No	○ Yes ○ No
Amount now in fund?	$	$	$	$
Giving to worthy causes?	○ Yes ○ No	○ Yes ○ No	○ Yes ○ No	○ Yes ○ No
Using the buddy system?	○ Yes ○ No	○ Yes ○ No	○ Yes ○ No	○ Yes ○ No
Debts paid?	○ Yes ○ No	○ Yes ○ No	○ Yes ○ No	○ Yes ○ No
How much $$ so far?	$	$	$	$
3-6 months expenses saved?	○ Yes ○ No	○ Yes ○ No	○ Yes ○ No	○ Yes ○ No
How many months saved?				
Saving now for major purchases?	○ Yes ○ No	○ Yes ○ No	○ Yes ○ No	○ Yes ○ No
List types.				
Funding pre-tax savings?	○ Yes ○ No	○ Yes ○ No	○ Yes ○ No	○ Yes ○ No
College funding started?	○ Yes ○ No	○ Yes ○ No	○ Yes ○ No	○ Yes ○ No
Paying extra on mortgage?	○ Yes ○ No	○ Yes ○ No	○ Yes ○ No	○ Yes ○ No
Walking in Financial Peace?	○ Yes ○ No	○ Yes ○ No	○ Yes ○ No	○ Yes ○ No

Printed in China
08MCC010-02

FINANCIAL SNAPSHOT

CLASS START DATE (MM/DD/YY) ☐☐/☐☐/☐☐

CLASS LOCATION CODE ☐☐☐☐☐☐

FIRST NAME ☐☐☐☐☐☐☐☐☐☐☐☐☐☐☐

SPOUSE FIRST NAME ☐☐☐☐☐☐☐☐☐☐☐☐☐☐☐

LAST NAME: S P A R K E S

Dave Ramsey's **Financial Peace University**

COORDINATOR FIRST NAME

COORDINATOR LAST NAME

Complete information in column 1, session #3, based upon your current financial situation since you started applying the "Financial Peace" principles; even if you started applying them prior to taking the FPU class.

Areas to work on IMMEDIATELY	Session 3	Session 6	Session 9	Session 12
Have a budget that works?	○ Yes ○ No	○ Yes ○ No	○ Yes ○ No	○ Yes ○ No
Paying necessities before creditors?	● Yes ○ No	○ Yes ○ No	○ Yes ○ No	○ Yes ○ No
Cut up all credit cards?	○ Yes ● No	○ Yes ○ No	○ Yes ○ No	○ Yes ○ No
Living on envelope system?	● Yes ○ No	○ Yes ○ No	○ Yes ○ No	○ Yes ○ No
How many envelopes?	5			
$1000 in emergency fund?	● Yes ○ No	○ Yes ○ No	○ Yes ○ No	○ Yes ○ No
Amount now in fund?	$1000.00	$	$	$
Giving to worthy causes?	● Yes ○ No	○ Yes ○ No	○ Yes ○ No	○ Yes ○ No
Using the buddy system?	● Yes ○ No	○ Yes ○ No	○ Yes ○ No	○ Yes ○ No
Debts paid?	○ Yes ● No	○ Yes ○ No	○ Yes ○ No	○ Yes ○ No
How much $$ so far?	$ 415.00	$	$	$
3-6 months expenses saved?	○ Yes ● No	○ Yes ○ No	○ Yes ○ No	○ Yes ○ No
How many months saved?	0			
Saving now for major purchases?	○ Yes ● No	○ Yes ○ No	○ Yes ○ No	○ Yes ○ No
List types.				
Funding pre-tax savings?	○ Yes ● No	○ Yes ○ No	○ Yes ○ No	○ Yes ○ No
College funding started?	○ Yes ● No	○ Yes ○ No	○ Yes ○ No	○ Yes ○ No
Paying extra on mortgages?	○ Yes ● No	○ Yes ○ No	○ Yes ○ No	○ Yes ○ No
Walking in Financial Peace?	○ Yes ● No	○ Yes ○ No	○ Yes ○ No	○ Yes ○ No

Complete this form online in the Member Resource Center at http://www.daveramsey.com/fpumember

46094

Printed in China
06MCC010-02

FINANCIAL SNAPSHOT

Dave Ramsey's

Financial Peace University

CLASS START DATE (MM/DD/YY)

☐☐ / ☐☐ / ☐☐

CLASS LOCATION CODE

☐☐☐☐☐

FIRST NAME

☐☐☐☐☐☐☐☐☐☐☐☐

SPOUSE FIRST NAME

☐☐☐☐☐☐☐☐☐☐☐☐

LAST NAME

☐☐☐☐☐☐☐☐☐☐☐☐

COORDINATOR FIRST NAME

☐☐☐☐☐☐☐☐☐☐☐☐

COORDINATOR LAST NAME

☐☐☐☐☐☐☐☐☐☐☐☐☐☐☐☐☐☐☐☐

cash flow planning

Complete information in column 1, session #3, based upon your current financial situation since you started applying the "Financial Peace" principles; even if you started applying them prior to taking the FPU class.

Areas to work on IMMEDIATELY	Session 3	Session 6	Session 9	Session 12
Have a budget that works?	○ Yes ○ No	○ Yes ○ No	○ Yes ○ No	○ Yes ○ No
Paying necessities before creditors?	○ Yes ○ No	○ Yes ○ No	○ Yes ○ No	○ Yes ○ No
Cut up all credit cards?	○ Yes ○ No	○ Yes ○ No	○ Yes ○ No	○ Yes ○ No
Living on envelope system?	○ Yes ○ No	○ Yes ○ No	○ Yes ○ No	○ Yes ○ No
How many envelopes?	☐☐	☐☐	☐☐	☐☐
$1000 in emergency fund?	○ Yes ○ No	○ Yes ○ No	○ Yes ○ No	○ Yes ○ No
Amount now in fund?	$ ☐	$ ☐	$ ☐	$ ☐
Giving to worthy causes?	○ Yes ○ No	○ Yes ○ No	○ Yes ○ No	○ Yes ○ No
Using the buddy system?	○ Yes ○ No	○ Yes ○ No	○ Yes ○ No	○ Yes ○ No
Debts paid?	○ Yes ○ No	○ Yes ○ No	○ Yes ○ No	○ Yes ○ No
How much $$ so far?	$ ☐	$ ☐	$ ☐	$ ☐
3-6 months expenses saved?	○ Yes ○ No	○ Yes ○ No	○ Yes ○ No	○ Yes ○ No
How many months saved?	☐☐	☐☐	☐☐	☐☐
Saving now for major purchases?	○ Yes ○ No	○ Yes ○ No	○ Yes ○ No	○ Yes ○ No
List types.	☐	☐	☐	☐
Funding pre-tax savings?	○ Yes ○ No	○ Yes ○ No	○ Yes ○ No	○ Yes ○ No
College funding started?	○ Yes ○ No	○ Yes ○ No	○ Yes ○ No	○ Yes ○ No
Paying extra on mortgages?	○ Yes ○ No	○ Yes ○ No	○ Yes ○ No	○ Yes ○ No
Walking in Financial Peace?	○ Yes ○ No	○ Yes ○ No	○ Yes ○ No	○ Yes ○ No

Complete this form online in the Member Resource Center at http://www.daveramsey.com/fpumember

46094

✅ Discussion Questions

1. What are the benefits of a written cash flow plan? Be specific. How can this impact a marriage? How can it strengthen a single person?

2. What things have kept you from living by a cash flow plan?

3. Which marital partner in your situation needs to take responsibility in guiding your plan? What if neither of you likes working with numbers?

4. What should you do if you are single and hate working with numbers or budgets?

Answer Key (left to right)			
Active	Cash	Flow	Checkbook
Living	Carbon	ATM	Debit
Bread	Water	Abuse	Worked
Fear	Leave	Out	Complicate
Do	Live	Crisis	Farther
Money	Fights	Guilt	Shame
Fear	Bounced	Checks	Stress
Over	Spending	Zero	Envelope

 # Accountability Check-Up
Cash Flow Planning

I. Everyone holds up his/her BASIC QUICKIE BUDGET to show you that they worked on it. Use the Quickie Budget to help you do your first zero-based budget.

II. CLASS COMMITMENTS
   A. Everyone makes a verbal commitment that they will start putting something aside for an emergency fund each month, even if it is only $4. It is vitally important to your financial future that you get into the habit of making this a priority!
   B. Everyone makes a commitment to the group to attend all 13 class sessions, unless an emergency comes up.
   C. Explain the FINANCIAL SNAPSHOT form and tell families they will be completing the first column after the next class.

III. Have each person/family make a commitment to go home and do a ZERO-BASED BUDGET before the next class session.

(handwritten: due 10/3/07 Pg55)

IV. ACCOUNTABILITY & APPLICATION REVIEW: (Everyone reads and comments on these statements.)
   A. I understand the concept behind how to use the cash envelope system and will commit to using at least one envelope for food throughout this program. (Instructions are in the envelope system.)
   B. I have balanced my checking account this month.
       (See sample "How to Balance Your Checkbook" in this lesson, if necessary.)
   C. Why is writing post dated or "warm" checks a bad idea?
   D. I will not impulse shop anymore or use my ATM or debit card impulsively.
   E. What are some potential benefits to your family of having a written budget? Based on benefits, I will make a commitment right now to myself (and my spouse, if married) and to this group, that I will do three monthly zero-based budgets during this 13-week program (blank forms are located in the back starting on page 253).
   F. Does anyone have any questions about how to do a budget? (Review as a group if needed.)

V. Be prepared to show your ZERO-BASED BUDGET at the next class.

●●

Member
RESOURCE CENTER
DaveRamsey.com/FPUMember

* Be sure to complete your homework the easy way online, and get great financial tools and resources for this week's lesson.
* Log in using your class code on page 22.

Our Guarantee

cash flow planning

If you do it,
IT WORKS!

If you don't do it,
IT WON'T WORK!

*If you will work
the program,*
**YOU WON'T WANT YOUR
MONEY BACK.**

*If you don't work
the program,*
**YOU DON'T GET YOUR
MONEY BACK.**

Dave Ramsey's

Financial Peace University

Relating With Money

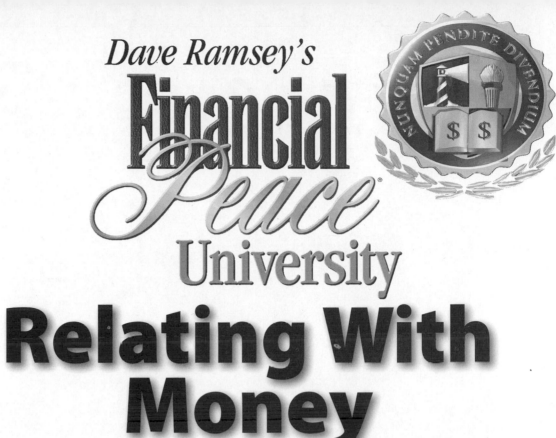

Travis Foster

"Personal relationships are the fertile soil from which all advancement, all success, all achievement in real life grows."

Ben Stein

✓ Notes:

Relating With Money

✓ Relating With Money

The flow of money in a family represents the ___Value___ ___System___ under which that family is operating.

Men, Women, and Money (overgeneralizing)

Emergency Fund Savings:

- Men: "Boring, not sophisticated ___Enough___."

- Women: "Most ___Important___ key to our financial plan."

Shopping:

- Men get good deals by ___Negotiating___.

- Men want to win.

- Women get good deals by ___Hunting___.

- Women enjoy the process.

Financial Problems:

- Men lose _Self_ - _Esteem_, because with men, money usually represents a _Score Card_.

- Women face _fear_ or even _Terror_, because usually with women, money can represent _Security_.

> *How many marriages would be better if the husband and the wife actually understood that they're on the same side?*

Marriages and Money

Can We Talk?

- The number-one cause of divorce in America today is _Money Fights_

- As you learn to discuss major purchases and budgets and come to agreement, you are agreeing on your _Value System_.

Relating With Money

- When this happens, you will reach a ___UNITY___ in your marriage that you can experience no other way.

> *"The happiest people in the world are those who do the most for others."*
> *Booker T. Washington*

> *"Therefore, a man shall leave his father and mother and be joined to his wife, and they shall become one flesh."*
>
> *Genesis 2:24 (NKJV)*

Who Does the Financial Decision Making?

- Both ___Both___ ___Both___ !!!

- The partner with the natural ___Gift___ can prepare the ___Budget___, but the decision making must be by ___Both___.

- The ___Bill (nerd)___ likes doing the budget because it gives him/her control, and he/she feels like they are taking care of loved ones.

> *"With all lowliness and gentleness, with long-suffering, bearing with one another in love, endeavoring to keep the unity of the Spirit in the bond of peace."*
>
> *Ephesians 4:2-3 (NKJV)*

- The ___free___ spirit feels controlled (not cared for) and can appear irresponsible to the nerd.

Singles and Their Money

- Time _Poverty_ (no time) and fatigue can lead to poor money management.

- Beware of _Impulse_ buying which can be brought on by _Stress_ or even by the "I owe it to _Myself_" syndrome.

- A written plan gives the _Single_ person empowerment, self accountability and _Control_.

Prevention

- Develop an _ACCOUNTABILITY_ relationship.

- Someone with whom to discuss major _Purchases_.

- Someone with whom to discuss your _BUDGET_.

- Accountability friends must love you enough to be brutally honest and promise to do so for your own good.

Suggested possibilities: pastor, parent, relative, boss, etc.

Teach the Children

- The teaching of fiscal responsibility is not the _Schools_ responsibility. It is _Your_ responsibility!

> "Train up a child in the way he should go, and when he is old, he will not depart from it. The rich rule over the poor and the borrower is servant to the lender."
>
> Proverbs 22:6-7 (NKJV)

> "Tell me, and I'll forget. Show me, and I may not remember. Involve me, and I'll understand."
>
> Native American Saying

> "But if anyone does not provide for his own, and especially for those of his household, he has denied the faith and is worse than an unbeliever."
>
> I Timothy 5:8 (NKJV)

- Pay _Commission_ not allowance; we have enough people in our society who expect to be made allowance for.

- Words are _Powerful_.

> "Criticize the performance, not the performer."
>
> Anonymous

> "Correct your son, and he will give you rest; yes, he will give delight to your soul."
>
> Proverbs 29:17 (NKJV)

- If you _Work_ you eat; if you do not _Work_ you do not eat.

> "For even when we were with you, we commanded you this: If anyone will not work, neither shall he eat."
>
> II Thessalonians 3:10 (NKJV)

- Teach by _EXAMPLE_.

- Show them how you live _DEBT_ free, how insurance works, how an IRA works, etc.

> "The silver haired head is a crown of glory, if it is found in the way of righteousness."
>
> Proverbs 16:31 (NKJV)

- If the children are young, use a clear _CONTAINER_ to save.

- The visual reinforcement is powerful.

Relating With Money

- Use three envelopes for ages _5–12_ :
  GIVING *(#1)*, spending, and saving *(#3)*. (Check out our teaching kit for children called Financial Peace Jr.)

- Somewhere around _13–15_ years old open a checking account for the child and teach him how to run it by monthly reviews.

- A great saving exercise is to have the child save to buy her first _CAR_. *PAY CASH & MATCH*

A Very Good Idea

- What if your children had a _College_ fund and a _Debt_ _free_ fund?

- Coupled with a commitment from your children to never borrow, this idea could change your family tree.

Discussion Questions

1. What are the advantages to being single in regards to financial control? What are the disadvantages?

2. What are some of the reasons that finances should be agreed on by both partners in a marriage?

3. What are some of the ways your parents did or did not teach you about money, saving, and work?

4. What are some practical things you can do with teenagers to teach the lost art of personal finance?

Answer Key (left to right)		
Value	System	Enough
Important	Negotiating	Hunting
Self	Esteem	Scorecard
Fear	Terror	Security
Money	Fights	Value
System	Unity	Both
Both	Gift	Budget
Both	Nerd	Free
Poverty	Impulse	Stress
Myself	Single	Control
Accountability	Purchases	Budget
School's	Your	Commissions
Powerful	Work	Work
Example	Debt	Container
5-12	Giving	13-15
Car	College	Debt
Free		

✔ Accountability Check-Up

Relating With Money

I.   Everyone holds up Monthly ZERO-BASED BUDGET. Check each other
      for zero-based totals on the third page.
      A.   If you have debt, what does it do to your stress level?
      B.   Encourage each other to make a commitment to do everything possible to avoid
           adding any new debts to their financial picture.

II.   Have some fun with the class: Everyone can start bringing in their credit card applications.
      Add up the total credit limits that are being offered, then tear up the applications, or send
      them back with a copy of the Credit Rebellion Letter from our website. **Keep a running
      total for the group as a whole to see how much debt your class is avoiding by not accepting
      the credit cards. TOTALS WILL BE REVIEWED DURING SESSION #11.

III. ACCOUNTABILITY & APPLICATION REVIEW: (Everyone reads and comments about
      these statements.)
      A.   I put relationships above money – my spouse, children, and co-workers are more
           important than money or financial stress. (Would others - your friends or coworkers
           - agree with your answer?)
      B.   As a single parent, discuss how fatigue can affect your money management.
      C.   I am, or will start, having a quiet time each day to prioritize the most important
           things in my life and grow spiritually.
      D.   How long did it take you to reach your current financial situation? Based on that, how
           long do you think it will take you to get out of debt? (If you have debt.)
      E.   Why is this important to teach your kids about money? What could happen if you do
           not? Make a commitment to teach your children what you are learning from
           Financial Peace.
      F.   As you have probably already seen, personal finance is about behavior. Please make a
           commitment to keep the families in your class in your thoughts and prayers.
      G.   Is it easier to impulse shop as a single person, without someone to answer to?

* Be sure to complete your financial snapshot and homework
  the easy way online, and get great financial tools and resources
  for this week's lesson.
* Log in using your class code on page 22.

✔ A Story of Deliverance and a Financial Healing

(1) "A certain woman of the wives of the sons of the prophets cried out to Elisha, saying "Your servant my husband is dead, and you know that your servant feared the Lord. And the creditor is coming to take my two sons to be his slaves."

(2) So Elisha said to her, "What shall I do for you? Tell me, what do you have in the house?" and she said, "Your maidservant has nothing in the house but a jar of oil."

(3) Then he said, "Go, borrow vessels from everywhere, from all your neighbors - empty vessels; do not gather just a few.

(4) And when you have come in, you shall shut the door behind you and your sons; then pour into all those vessels, and set aside the full ones."

(5) So she went from him and shut the door behind her and her sons, who brought the vessels to her; and she poured it out.

(6) Now it came to pass, when the vessels were full, that she said to her son, "Bring me another vessel." And he said to her, "There is not another vessel." So the oil ceased.

(7) Then she came and told the man of God. And he said, "Go, sell the oil and pay your debt; and you and your sons live on the rest."

II Kings 4:1-7 (NKJV)

Relating With Money

Dave Ramsey's

Financial *Peace* University

Buying Only Big, Big Bargains

Travis Foster

"Probably the world's greatest humorist was the man who named them easy payments."

Stanislas

Notes:

big, big bargains

Big, Big Bargains

Buying Only Big, Big Bargains

It is proper to get a great deal if you:

1) Have in no way _Misrepresented_ the truth.

2) Have not set out to _HARM_ the other party.

3) Have created a win _WIN_ deal.

The First Key

- The First Key to opening the door to huge bargains is you must negotiate _Everything_.

- Win _WIN_ really works so don't be _AFRAID_ to ask for the _DEAL_!

Lucky Seven Basic Rules of Negotiating

> *"A false balance is an abomination to the Lord, but a just weight is His delight."*
>
> *Proverbs 11:1 (NKJV)*

> *"He who sells what isn't his'n, buys it back or goes to pris'n."*
>
> *Anonymous*

1. Always tell the absolute ___*TRUETH*___ .

2. Use the power of ___*CASH*___ .
   Cash is: 1) ___*EMOTIONAL*___
   2) ___*VISUAL*___
   3) (has) ___*IMMEDIACY*___

3. Understand and use "Walkaway ___*Power*___ ."

4. ___*SHUT*___ up.

5. "That is not ___*GOOD*___ enough." — *Shut up & they will come down. Car sales. See How far they come down before they stop.*

6. ___*Good*___ guy, ___*Buy*___ guy.

7. The "If I" take ___*Away*___ technique.

"Millionar Next Door"
Books Stanley
Tom
Millionar MIND

INTEGRITY IS
#1 FACTOR of
Millionary

big, big bargains

The Second Key

- The Second Key to opening the door to huge bargains is that you must have _PATIENCE_.

- Don't get _MARRIED_ to a purchase.

> *"Remember, what you possess in the world will be found at the day of your death to belong to someone else, but what you are will be yours forever."*
>
> *Henry Van Dyke*

> *"But the fruit of the Spirit is love, joy, peace, patience, kindness, goodness, faithfulness."*
>
> *Galatians 5:22 (NIV)*

The Third Key

- The Third Key to opening the door to huge bargains is that you must know where to find _DEALS_.

- _TRADE_ something of value, goods or just your _Services_.

> *"A man who owns little is little owned."*
>
> *Anonymous*

Places to Find Great Deals

1. Estate Sales

2. Individuals

3. Auctions

4. Couponing

5. Garage Sales

6. Flea Market

7. Repo Lots

8. Refunding

9. Foreclosures

10. Pawn Shops

11. Classified Ads

12. Consignment Sales

13. Convention

Dont pay too much

Don't buy something you don't need

 **Love, Mom**

During a period of economic hardship due to high interest rates in the real estate business, my mother sent me the following poem in the mail, and it hangs on my office wall today.

THE ROOSTER AND THE HEN

Said the Little Red Rooster, "Believe me things are tough!
Seems the worms are getting scarcer and I cannot find enough.
What's become of all those fat ones? It's a mystery to me.
There were thousands through that rainy spell,
But now, where can they be?"

But the Old Black Hen who heard him didn't grumble or complain,
She had lived through lots of dry spells;
She had lived through floods of rain.
She picked a new and undug spot, The ground was hard and firm,
"I must go to the worms," she said. "The worms won't come to me."

The Rooster vainly spent his day,
Through habit, by the ways
Where fat round worms had passed in squads back in the rainy days.
When nightfall found him supperless, he growled in accents rough,
"I'm hungry as a fowl can be, conditions sure are tough."

But the Old Black Hen hopped to her perch
And dropped her eyes to sleep
And murmured in a drowsy tone, "Young man, hear this and weep.
I'm full of worms and happy
For I've eaten like a pig.
The worms were there as always
But, boy I had to dig!"

This was a Depression Era Poem. Strange it still applies today.

Love,

Mom

☑ Discussion Questions

1. Why do we feel guilty when getting a bargain?

2. What phenomenon in our society has caused us to move away from bargain hunting?

3. Why do we many times avoid negotiation?

4. What are some great bargains you have gotten and locations you know where bargains can be had?

Answer Key (left to right)		
Misrepresented	Harm	Win
Everything	Win	Afraid
Deal	Truth	Cash
Emotional	Visual	Immediacy
Power	Shut	Good
Good	Bad	Away
Patience	Married	Deals
Trade	Services	Estate Sales
Individuals	Public Auctions	Couponing
Garage Sales/Yard	Flea Markets	Repo Lot
Refunding	Foreclosures	Pawn Shops
Classified Ads	Consignment Sales	

Big, Big Bargains

# ✔ Accountability Check-Up

Buying Only Big, Big Bargains

I.   Have everyone discuss how their envelope system is working for him/her. (How many are you using and for which categories? How has it helped? Have you found yourself thinking more about purchases?)

II. Encourage each other to invite another family to attend <u>one</u> of the classes with you for "Free" to see how this program can become a blessing in their life.

III. ACCOUNTABILITY & APPLICATION REVIEW: (Get into each other's hearts and help one another.)

    A. I/we have allocated all of this month's household income on paper <u>before</u> the month began.

    B. I/we have started saving money for an emergency fund.
        1. Ladies, talk about how important it is to you.
        2. Men, talk about how it makes you feel.
        3. Singles, talk about why you need an emergency fund.

    C. When I'm at a store and the cashier gives me back too much money I:
        1. Keep it and do not say anything (it's a blessing from God).
        2. Return it immediately.
        3. I never count my change to see if it's correct.

    D. With the Emergency Fund in place and a cash flow plan, I will cut up (destroy) all my credit cards because I no longer need them. I won't allow them to give me the opportunity to stay in debt. (Plan on cutting up credit cards after the Dumping Debt lesson.)

    E. What could you sell to pay off debt? I will sell these items on or before (date).

    F. Why is it important to set aside a little "blow money" each month for myself (and my spouse) as my (our) budget permits to do whatever I (we) want with it? (The budget is to be a blessing, not a burden.) You will probably blow some money, so budget for it!

    G. Are you still plagued by impulsive purchases? Explain what happens inside you when you are tempted to spend!!!

• •

* Be sure to complete your homework the easy way online, and get great financial tools and resources for this week's lesson.
* Log in using your class code on page 22.

HAS FPU BECOME A BLESSING IN YOUR LIFE?

THEN FEEL FREE TO INVITE A FRIEND OR LOVED ONE TO ATTEND ONE CLASS SESSION FOR FREE AS OUR GUEST!

Dave Ramsey's

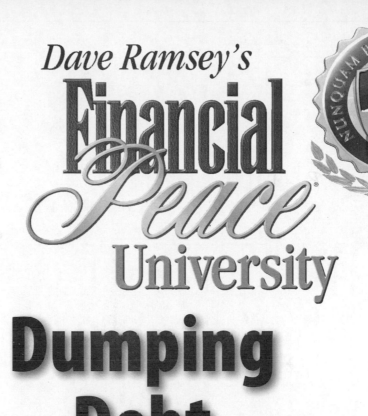

Dumping Debt

Travis Foster

"The rich rule over the poor, and the borrower is servant to the lender."

Proverbs 22:7 (NKJV)

Dumping Debt

 Debunking the Myth

- If you tell a lie or spread a _____ often enough, loud enough, and long enough, the myth becomes accepted as _____.

- Debt has been _____ to us in so many forms so aggressively since the 1960s that to even imagine living without it requires a complete paradigm _____.

Myth: If I loan money to a friend or relative I will be _HELPING_ them.

Truth: The relationship will be strained or _DESTROYED_ .

Myth: By cosigning a loan I am _HELPING_ out a friend or relative.

Truth: The bank requires a cosigner because the person isn't likely to _REPAY_ , so be ready to pay the loan and have your credit messed up because you are on the loan.

> *"It's stupid to guarantee someone else's loan."*
>
> *Proverbs 17:18 (CEV)*

Myth: Cash advance, rent-to-own, title pawning, and tote-the-note car lots are needed _Service's_ for lower income people to get ahead.

Truth: These are horrible, _Greedy_ rip-offs that aren't needed and benefit no one but the owners of these companies.

dumping debt

✅ Debunking the Myth

__Myth__: Playing the lotto and other forms of gambling will make me ___Rich___.

__Truth__: Lotto and Powerball are a tax on the poor and on people who can't do ___MATH___.

__Myth__: Car ___PAYMENTS___ are a way of life, and you'll always have one.

__Truth__: Staying away from car payments by driving reliable used cars is what the typical millionaire does. That is ___HOW___ they became millionaires.

__Myth__: ___Leasing___ your car is what sophisticated financial people do. You should always lease things that go down in value. There are tax advantages.

__Truth__: Consumer Reports, Smart Money magazine, and a good calculator will tell you that the car lease is the most ___Expensive___ way to finance and operate a vehicle.

__Truth__: If you own a business, you can write off your ___Paid For___ car on taxes without paying payments for the privilege.

__Truth__: The way to minimize the money lost on things that go down in value is to buy slightly ___USED___.

Ave car $
$ 378ᵃ /55 months

✓ Debunking the Myth

Myth: You can get a good deal on a <u>New</u> car.

Truth: A new car loses <u>60%</u> of it's value in the first four years. This is the largest purchase most consumers make that goes down in value.

> *A new car selling for $28,000 on average will lose $16,800 of it's value in the first four years, making it worth about $11,200. You are losing about $350 per month in value!*

Myth: The Home Equity Loan is good because of the <u>TAX</u> deduction and is a substitute for an emergency fund.

Truth: You don't go into <u>Debt</u> for emergencies.

Truth: A tax deduction is not good <u>MATH</u>.

> *If you have a loan of $50,000 at 10%, you would pay interest of $5,000 to the bank which you can deduct from your taxes if the loan is against your home. If you did not have this deduction and had to pay taxes on that $5,000 in a 25% bracket, you would pay $1,250 in taxes. So you are telling me that you would like to send the bank $5,000 to keep from sending Congress $1,250? Why don't you just give the $5,000 to your church, get the exact same tax benefit, and avoid the debt?*

dumping debt

 **Debunking the Myth**

Myth: I'll take out a 30-year mortgage and pay *Extra*, I promise.

Truth: Sick children, bad transmissions, prom dresses, downsizing, high utilities this month... do I really need to go on? No one ever pays extra every month. Never take more than a *15 yr* fixed-rate loan.

> *"Owe no one anything except to love one another..."*
>
> *Romans 13:8 (NKJV)*

Shorter Terms

Home Purchased	$90,000
Down Payment	$10,000
Mortgage Amount	$80,000

10% Interest

PAYMENT	TOTAL	PAY BACK
30 years	$702	$252,740
15 years	$859	$154,743
Difference	$157	$ 97,997

You Saved Almost $100,000!

✔ Debunking the Myth

Myth: It is _Good_ to take out an ARM or a balloon mortgage if "I know I'll be moving."

Truth: You will be moving when they _Foreclose_.

Myth: You need to take out a credit card or car loan to "build your _Credit_."

Truth: Open credit card accounts with zero balances count against you as well as car payments when qualifying for a home _Mortgage_.

> *With a 20% down payment, not buying too much house, two years or more on the job, and two years of paying your landlord early, you will qualify for a mortgage. Don't fall for the lie!!!*

Myth: You need a credit card to _Rent_ a car.

Truth: A _Debit_ card will work at all the major rentals with few exceptions. Check in advance.

dumping debt

Myth: You need a _CREDIT_ card to check into a hotel or to make a purchase by phone or over the Web.

Truth: A _Debit_ card will do all of that.

Myth: "I pay mine off every _MONTH_ with no annual fee. I get brownie points, air miles, and a free hat."

Truth: 78% of Americans do not pay off the balance EVERY _MONTH_.

Truth: A recent Dunn and Bradstreet _Study_ found that when paying cash (from your envelope system), you spend 12% to 18% less because spending cash hurts. Ouch! So what if you get 1% back and a free hat?!

Myth: I'll make sure my _Teenager_ gets a credit card so he/she can learn to be responsible with money.

Truth: Teens are the number-one _TARGET_ of credit card companies today. Anyone with half a brain realizes how stupid this myth is.

 **Debunking the Myth**

Myth: Debt consolidation _SAVES_ interest, and you get just one smaller payment.

Truth: Debt consolidation is a _Con_.

Truth: Debt consolidation typically saves _Little_ or no interest because you will throw your low interest loans into the deal.

Truth: You can't borrow your way out of _Debt_.

Truth: Smaller payments equal more time in _Debt_.

Myth: Debt is a _Tool_ and should be used to create prosperity.

Truth: Debt is proof that the borrower is slave to the _Lender_.

Truth: When surveyed, the Forbes 400 were asked, "What is the most important key to building wealth?" _75%_ replied that becoming and staying debt-free was the number one key to building wealth.

How much could you _SAVE_, invest, blow and _Give_ if you had no payments?

dumping debt

✓ Steps Out of Debt

1. Quit ___BORROWING___ more ___Money___!!!

> *"If you want to get yourself better off financially, QUIT BUYING THINGS!"*
>
> **Anonymous**

2. You must ___SAVE___ money.

3. ___PRAYER___ really works.

4. Sell ___SOMETHING___.

5. Part-time ___JOB___ or overtime (temporarily).

6. Debt ___SNOWBALL___.

dumping debt

Dumping Debt

✔ Credit Card Crumbs

According to *USA Today*, 63% of bankruptcy filers blame credit card bills and 89% of filers STILL get offers.

Bank credit card balances **per U.S. household hit $8,000** during 2005 according to a recent story on pbs.org.

Ram Research Corporation states there are over **50 million** Discover cards, **49 million** Citibank Visas, and **48 million** American Express.

According to the *Wall Street Journal* there are over **63 million Sears** cards with over 700,000 applications per month.

Credit card issuers sent out **4 billion** pieces of mail last year to **93 million households**, which is an average of more than **43 offers** going to each household, as reported in *Ladies Home Journal*.

Capitol One and MBNA, two of the major issuers, spend **$60-$70 million each quarter** on credit card offers, according to CardWeb, Inc.

USA Today notes that Citibank, the largest issuer of Visa, will spend **$100 million** this year just **marketing** credit cards to your **high school** and **college students.**

Colleges can earn $50,000 to $100,000 per year just to allow a credit card company to operate on campus. **Credit cards have become a rite of passage into adulthood.**

According to American Express, **33% of consumers use plastic more** frequently today than **five years ago.**

According to the Federal Reserve Board, consumers' outstanding debt on credit cards and other revolving loans has grown continuously over the last decade hitting **$1.5 trillion *last year.***

Sample Debt Snowball

Sheet 10

    List your debts in order from smallest to largest with the smallest payoff or balance first. Do not be concerned with interest rates or terms unless two debts have similar payoffs, then list the higher interest rate debt first. Paying the little debts off first shows you quick feedback, and you are more likely to stay with the plan.

    Redo this sheet each time you pay off a debt so you can see how close you are getting to freedom. Keep the old sheets to wallpaper the bathroom in your new debt-free house. The "New Payment" is found by adding all the payments on the debts listed above that item to the payment you are working on, so you have compounding payments which will get you out of debt very quickly. "Payments Remaining" is the number of payments remaining on that debt when you get down the snowball to that item. Cumulative Payments is the total payments needed, including the snowball, to pay off that item. In other words, this is your running total for "Payments Remaining."

COUNT DOWN TO FREEDOM!!

Date:_____

Item	Total Payoff	Minimum Payment	New Payment	Payments Remaining	Cumulative Payments
Penny's	$150	$15	$0	0	Garage Sale
Sears	$250	$10	$25	11	11
Visa	$500	$75	$100	PD	11
M.C.	$1500	$90	$190	5	16
Car	$4000	$210	$400	4	20
Stu. Loans	$4000	$65	$465	6	26

TOTALLY Debt Free except the house!
    Finish Emergency Fund
    Fund Retirement/College
    Then Do House

dumping debt

The Debt Snowball

Sheet 10

List your debts in order from smallest to largest with the smallest payoff or balance first. Do not be concerned with interest rates or terms unless two debts have similar payoffs, then list the higher interest rate debt first. Paying the little debts off first shows you quick feedback, and you are more likely to stay with the plan.

Redo this sheet each time you pay off a debt so you can see how close you are getting to freedom. Keep the old sheets to wallpaper the bathroom in your new debt-free house. The "New Payment" is found by adding all the payments on the debts listed above that item to the payment you are working on, so you have compounding payments which will get you out of debt very quickly. "Payments Remaining" is the number of payments remaining on that debt when you get down the snowball to that item. Cumulative Payments is the total payments needed, including the snowball, to pay off that item. In other words, this is your running total for "Payments Remaining."

COUNT DOWN TO FREEDOM!!

Date:_____

Item	Total Payoff	Minimum Payment	New Payment	Payments Remaining	Cumulative Payments

☑ Discussion Questions

1. What got you started spending on credit?

2. Describe what feelings you would have if you had no debt.

3. How would your life change if you had no debt? Be specific.

4. What would you do with the money that is freed up?

Answer Key (left to right)			
Myth	Truth	Marketed	Shift
Helping	Destroyed	Helping	Repay
Services	Greedy	Rich	Math
Payments	How	Leasing	Expensive
Paid-For	Used	New	60%
Tax	Debt	Math	Extra
15-Year	Good	Foreclose	Credit
Mortgage	Rent	Debit	Credit
Debit	Month	Month	Study
Teenager	Target	Saves	Con
Little	Debt	Debt	Tool
Lender	75%	Save	Give
Borrowing	Money	Save	Prayer
Something	Job	Snowball	

Dumping Debt

Accountability Check-Up

(handwritten, circled: chapt. 7 & 8)

Dumping Debt

I. Be prepared to cut up your credit cards tonight!

    A. You will never fully remove debt from your life as long as you hold on to any credit cards.

    B. Make a commitment to never use credit cards again.

II. ACCOUNTABILITY & APPLICATION REVIEW: (No beating around the bush.)

    A. (True or False) If you have $1,000 in an emergency fund and have a debit card, there is no good reason/excuse for keeping a credit card, according to the Financial Peace principles. Why?

    B. Which myth did you buy into before this lesson?

    C. I am honest with myself (and my spouse, if applicable) regarding how I (we) handle financial affairs. Why is this important?

    D. Does everyone fully understand how to put together and work the Debt Snowball?

    E. I will go home and put together the Debt Snowball this week and start applying it to my financial situation.

    F. How many of us currently have or have had a CONsolidation loan? Did you discover it really was a con?

    G. Why is gazelle intensity so important to your journey to Financial Peace? Make a commitment to have gazelle intensity and deliver yourself (and family) from the burden and bondage of debt.

    H. I truly take this program seriously and am applying the principles to my life.

    I. When you hear the phrase "...the borrower is servant to the lender," how does it make you feel?

    J. Before going through this program, did you realize that the way you handle your money is really a spiritual issue?

III. REVIEW DISCUSSION QUESTIONS at the end of the lesson.

IV. Go home and complete the credit card history form on page 120. Use the form to help you close your credit card accounts as soon as possible.

* Be sure to complete your homework the easy way online, and get great financial tools and resources for this week's lesson.
* Log in using your class code on page 22.

dumping debt

Credit Card History

CARD NAME	NUMBER	ADDRESS	PHONE #	DATE CLOSED	WRITTEN CONFIRMATION REQUESTED	WRITTEN CONFIRMATION RECIEVED
Mastercard	5555 5555 5555 5555	111 Credit Blvd., New York, NY	(201) 758-2222	8/14/2006	7/14/2006	8/28/2006

120

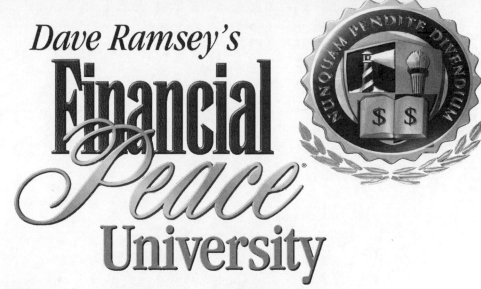

Dave Ramsey's
Financial Peace University

Understanding Investments

Travis Foster

"The plans of the diligent lead surely to plenty, But those of everyone who is hasty, surely to poverty"

Proverbs 21:5 (NKJV)

Notes:

Understanding Investments

Understanding Investments

KISS Rule of Investing

- Keep it _Simple_ _Stupid_ .

- It does not indicate that you are stupid if you make _Stupid_ investments.

- _Never_ invest purely for tax savings.

- _Never_ invest using _Borrowed_ money.

Diversification

- Diversification means to _Spread_ _Around_ .

- Diversification _Lowers_ risk.

> "Give portions to seven, yes to eight, for you do not know what disaster may come upon the land."
>
> Ecclesiastes 11:2 (NIV)

Grandma used to say, "Don't put all your eggs in one basket." That way if you dropped the basket, not all your eggs would be broken. Investing is the same way. Don't put all your money into one investment.

The Power of Diversification

(handwritten note) NEED AT LEAST A 6% interest. if 5years or longer becore of IN DATION of 4.2% you are losing TAX's

Investor 1
Invest $10,000 for 25 years at 7%

Investor 2
Invest $2,000 and lose it all
Invest $2,000 under your mattress
Invest $2,000 at 5% return
Invest $2,000 and got a 10% return
Invest $2,000 and got a 15% return

Leave it alone for 25 years

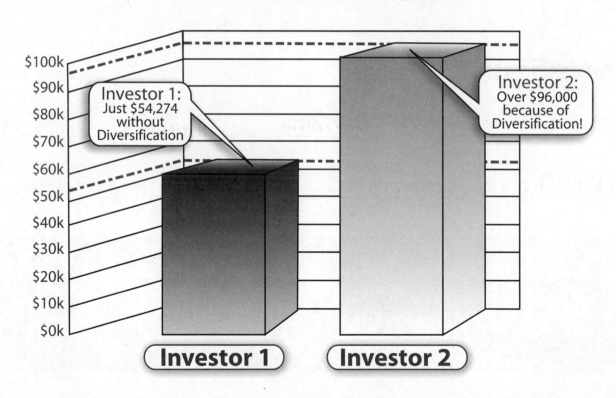

$54,274 Without Diversification; $96,280 Diversified
77% Difference

Understanding Investments

Understanding Investments

Risk Return Ratio

> *"Behold the turtle who only makes progress when he sticks his neck out."*
>
> *Anonymous*

> *"A faithful man will abound with blessings, but he who hastens to be rich will not go unpunished."*
>
> *Old Proverb*

- With virtually all investments, as the ___*Risk*___ goes up, so does the hopeful ___*Return*___.

- When discussing investments, liquidity is ___*Availability*___.

- As there is more liquidity, there is typically ___*less*___ return.

Types of Investments

1. Money Markets

- A C.D. is a certificate of ___*Deposit*___, typically at a bank.

- Money market mutual funds are ___*Low*___ risk money market accounts that you can write checks on and are great for emergency funds.

2. Single Stocks

> *"October. This is one of the peculiarly dangerous months to speculate in stocks. The others are July, January, September, April, November, May, March, June, December, August, and February."*
>
> *Mark Twain*

- The average investor makes a _____7_____ % return on his single stock portfolio with a very ___HIGH___ degree of risk.

- When you buy stock you are buying a small piece of ___Ownership___ in the company.

- Your return comes as the company increases in ___Value___ or pays you, it's owner, some of the profits (called ___Dividends___).

3. Bonds

- A bond is a ___Debt___ instrument where the company owes ___You___ money.

- Your return is the fluctuation in price and the ___Interest___ rate paid. ___Few___ individuals do well with single ___Bond___ purchases.

Understanding Investments

✔ Long Term Investments Properly Diversified

Standard Diversification

25%	Growth & Income
25%	Growth
25%	International
25%	Aggressive Growth

Conservative Diversification

25%	Balanced
25%	Growth & Income
25%	Growth
25%	International

SMALL CAP — EMERGING — AGRESSIVE Growth.

127

4. Mutual Funds

"An investment in knowledge always pays the best interest."

Ben Franklin

- Investors pool their _Money_ to invest.

- Professional portfolio managers manage the pool or _Fund_.

- Your return comes as the _Value_ of the fund is _Increased_.

- Mutual funds are good _Long_ term investments.

5. Rental Real Estate

- Least liquid consumer _Investment_.

- You should have a lot of _Cash_ before using real estate as an investment.

Teachers & Hospitals Have Mutual Funds

Growth Stock 97% 100%

Mutual Fund made money in 5 yrs. " " " 10 "

Don't Buy → Buy Options → Day Trading

Understanding Investments

6. Annuities

- Annuities are ___SAVINGS___ accounts with an insurance company.

- ___FIXED___ annuities are at a <u>low</u> interest rate of around 5%, aren't fixed, and are a <u>bad long-term</u> investment.

- ___VARIABLE___ annuities are mutual funds sheltered by the annuity covering allowing the mutual fund to <u>grow tax deferred</u>.

> *Variable annuities are good to use for older people because the principal can be guaranteed. You can name a beneficiary so the money passes outside probate, and you can use them when you have maxed out all your other sheltered retirement options. NEVER use annuities inside retirement options; instead, go straight to mutual funds. There is no sense paying the annuity fee to get a tax deferment that you already have in your retirement plan.*

7. Commodities and Futures

- Very, ___Very___ high degree of ___Risk___.

- You have a better chance in ___Las Vegas___.

Conclusion

If you do not understand an investment well enough to teach someone else about how it works, DON'T BUY IT!!

Build wealth slowly.

Monthly Debt Payments Rob You of Your Retirement!

Monthly Payments	5	10	15	25	40
$100	8,167	23,004	49,958	187,885	1,176,477
$200	16,334	46,008	99,916	375,769	2,352,954
$300	24,500	69,012	149,874	563,654	3,529,431
$400	32,668	92,015	199,832	751,538	4,705,909
$500	40,835	115,019	249,790	939,423	5,882,386
$600	49,002	138,023	299,748	1,127,308	7,058,863
$700	57,168	161,027	349,706	1,315,193	8,235,341
$800	65,336	184,031	399,664	1,503,077	9,411,818
$900	73,503	207,034	449,622	1,690,962	10,588,295
$1,000	81,669	230,039	499,580	1,878,847	11,764,772
$1,200	98,004	276,046	599,496	2,254,616	14,117,727
$1,500	122,504	345,058	749,370	2,818,270	17,647,159
$2,000	163,339	460,077	999,160	3,757,693	23,529,545

Years Invested Monthly at 12% Per Year

However, **retirement** can look pretty **sweet** if you don't have any debt.

Understanding Investments

I am your greatest helper or your heaviest burden.
I will push you onward or drag you down to failure.
I am at your command.
Half of the tasks that you do, you might just as well
turn over to me, and I will do them quickly and correctly.

I am easily managed. You must merely be firm with me.
Show me exactly how you want something done;
after a few lessons I will do it automatically.
I am the servant of all great people and alas of all
failures as well.
Those who are great I have made great,
Those who are failures I have made failures.

I am not a machine,
but I work with all the precision of a machine,
plus the intelligence of a person.
Now, you may run me for profit or
you may run me for ruin.
It makes no difference to me.
Take me, train me, be firm with me,
and I will lay the world at your feet.
Be easy with me, and I will destroy you.

WHO AM I?… I AM CALLED HABIT.

Author Unknown

I discovered this little gem at a seminar a few
years ago, and it applies here.

Discussion Questions

1.   Why is investing intimidating?

2.   Discuss some experiences with investing.

3.   Discuss Mutual Funds.

Answer Key (left to right)

Simple	Stupid	Simple
Never	Never	Borrowed
Spread	Around	Lowers
Risk	Return	Availability
Less	Deposit	Low
7%	High	Ownership
Value	Dividends	Debt
You	Interest	Few
Bond	Money	Fund
Value	Increased	Long
Investment	Cash	Savings
Fixed	Variable	Very
Risk	Las Vegas	

✓ Accountability Check-Up
Understanding Investments

I. Be prepared to show your filled in Debt Snowball form.
   A. EMOTION – EMOTION – EMOTION is the KEY! GET MAD!!!
   B. Use the combination of the Debt Snowball and emotion to motivate you to financial victories.
   C. Living by and committing to do the Debt Snowball will prove to be the difference between your success and failure.

II. Everyone needs to do their next month's budget and bring it next week. Be sure to make any adjustments necessary from the last budget you did.
   A. Use the Actually Spent column on the monthly budget sheet to help you with your next budget.
   B. It may be helpful for you to compare your actual percentage of take-home expenses with the recommended percentage chart.

III. Show your Financial Snapshot with Column 2 completed.

IV. ACCOUNTABILITY & APPLICATION REVIEW:
   A. Discuss why it's important to dump debt before starting to invest.
   B. Talk about the temptation of wanting to invest now instead of first dumping your debt, as we teach in Baby Step 2.
   C. What two words should you say to an investment broker who doesn't take the time to teach you about how your investments work? ("You're fired!")
   D. Talk about how important it is for spouses to be on the same page and working together when it comes to dumping debt and investing.
   E. Discuss the challenges of being single while trying to be accountable for your financial actions.
   F. Look at the "Monthly Debt Payments Rob You…" chart at the end of the lesson. Discuss how monthly debt robs people of the ability to invest monthly for their retirement.
   G. Discuss the danger of trying to invest using borrowed money.
   H. Talk about the Power of Diversification (see chart in the lesson). Is it wise to put all your eggs in one basket?
   I. What are the differences between saving and investing?

* Be sure to complete your financial snapshot and homework the easy way online, and get great financial tools and resources for this week's lesson.
* Log in using your class code on page 22.

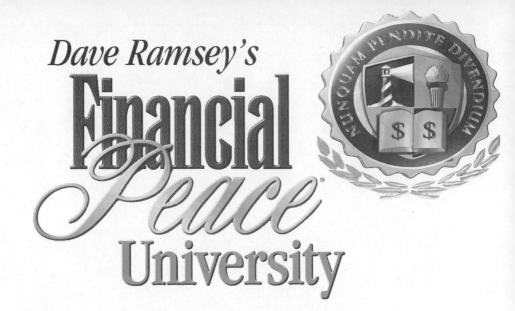

Dave Ramsey's
Financial Peace University

Understanding Insurance

Travis Foster

"It is unwise to hope for the best without preparing for the worst."

Anonymous

Understanding Insurance

✓ Understanding Insurance

Insurance is an essential financial planning tool.

The purpose of insurance is to _____ risk.

Until you have big, big cash, certain losses could bankrupt you, so wisdom says to transfer the _____.

> *"A prudent man sees evil and hides himself; the naive proceed and pay the penalty."*
>
> *Old Proverb*

Basic Types of Coverage Needed

1. _____ or _____ insurance

2. _____ insurance

3. _____ insurance

4. _____ insurance

5. _____ insurance

6. _____ insurance

# Types of Insurance

• Homeowners and Auto Insurance

1. Raise your _____ (savings should be there).

2. Carry adequate _____ .

3. Consider dropping your _____ on older cars.

4. Homeowners should be _____ cost.

5. _____liability policies are a good buy once you have some assets.

• Health Insurance

Keys to saving on your health premiums:

1. Increase your _____ and/or coinsurance amount.

2. Increase your_____ -loss but never decrease your maximum pay.

The self-employed can save money by using an _____, a Medical Savings Account (nicknamed Medical IRA).
  ** See page 262 for a note about the HSA.**

The MSA is a tax deductible medical savings account for medical bills that works with a _____ deductible (inexpensive) medical insurance policy.

Understanding Insurance

Understanding Insurance

• Disability Insurance

Disability insurance is designed to replace _____ lost due to a short-term or permanent disability.

Buy disability insurance that pays if you cannot perform the job that you were educated or _____ to do.

That is called _____ disability.

Buy coverage to age 65 or for _____.

Beware of _____ term policies.

Your coverage should be for _____% of your take-home pay.

The _____ period is how long before payments begin after disability.

The _____ the elimination period, the _____ your premium cost should be.

• Long-Term Care Insurance

Long-term care insurance is for _____ home or in-home care.

_____of people over the age of 65 will require long-term care at some point in their lives with _____ needing more than five years of care.

● Life Insurance

Everyone is going to die someday, but rarely do we know when that time is going to come. If people depend on you to provide an income, it is wise to insure your income in case you should lose your life.

Life insurance is to replace lost income due to _____.

It is really _____ insurance.

Most people have no _____ what they _____.

Two Types of Life Insurance:

1. _____ insurance is for a specified period, is substantially cheaper, and has no savings plan built into it.

2. _____ _____ insurance is normally for life and is more expensive in order to fund a savings plan.

The most common insurance myth is that the need for life insurance is a _____ situation and ever growing.

Twenty years from today, the children are grown and gone, and you are debt-free (including that old 15-year mortgage), and you have investments that have grown to a substantial amount. You have become self-_____.

Understanding Insurance

Understanding Insurance

Why not Life Insurance as an Investment?

1. Returns are historically _____.

2. When you die with cash value, the insurance company _____ the cash value.

3. The _____ deducted from your return are _____.

What to Remember When Purchasing Life Insurance:

1. Buy only low-cost level _____.

2. Do not forget your _____.

3. Stay away from fancy _____.

4. Children only need enough for _____ expenses.
   (They don't earn an income which needs replacement.)

How Much Insurance Do You Need?

You need about 10 times what your annual need would be if you lost that person. Invested at 10% return the investment would produce an income to cover the need.

Approximate Term Insurance Cost

Age 30 - $ 0.60 per $1,000 in coverage
Age 40 - $ 0.90 per $1,000 in coverage
Age 50 - $ 2.50 per $1,000 in coverage
Age 60 - $ 6.65 per $1,000 in coverage

* 20-year level term
* Tobacco users add 100%

Insurance Calculation

of Thousands X Rate per $1,000 = Total

Primary _____ X _____ = _____

Spouse _____ X _____ = _____

Est. Total Premium _____

Understanding Insurance

Understanding Insurance

Insurance to Avoid

1. _____ life and _____ disability

2. Credit _____ protection

3. _____ and hospital indemnity

4. Accidental _____ insurance

5. Any insurance with _____ value, investment, or refund

6. Pre-paid _____ policies

7. Mortgage _____ insurance

8. Any kind of _____ coverage

> **FOOTNOTE:**
> The Medical Savings Account (MSA) is no longer available. A much better option, the Health Savings Account (HSA), has replaced the MSA. See an explanation in the addendum on page 262 and understand why Dave is even more excited about this!

✔ Discussion Questions

1. Why do we detest insurance?

2. What do you think is the average death claim paid to a widow in the U.S.?

3. Explain the difference between term and cash value life insurance?

Answer Key (left to right)

Transfer	Risk	Homeowner's	Renter's
Auto	Health	Disability	Life Long
Term Care	Deductible	Liability	Collision
Replacement	Umbrella	Deductible	Stop MSA
Large	Income	Trained	Occupational
Life	Short	65	Elimination
Longer	Lower	Nursing	60% 20%
Death	Death	Idea	Own Term
Cash	Value	Permanent	Insured
Low	Keeps	Fees	High Term
Spouse	Options	Burial	Credit
Credit	Card	Cancer	Death
Cash	Burial	Life	Duplicate

Understanding Insurance

✓ Accountability Check-Up
Understanding Insurance

I.   Everyone hold up his/her monthly zero-based budget.
   A. Discuss how much easier or harder it was to do this time compared to the first month. Be HONEST and TRANSPARENT with each other.
   B. Discuss what you have learned about how YOU handle money.

II. ACCOUNTABILITY & APPLICATION REVIEW:
   A. Discuss how having an emergency fund in place can affect your insurance premiums and deductibles.
   B. What do you do if money is tight, and you're having a hard time financially?
       1. Take a chance and drop your insurance until you've paid off your debts.
       2. Only put insurance on the individual who brings home the most income and pray nothing happens to the rest of the family.
       3. Make insurance coverage a priority to avoid a financial disaster.
   C. What could happen to you financially if you do not have the proper amount of insurance in place? (If anyone in the group has a nightmare story to relate to the group regarding this issue, please share it now!!!)
   D. Discuss how having (or not having) the proper amount of insurance in place makes you feel:
       1. Ladies, talk about how important it is to you.
       2. Men, talk about how it makes you feel.
       3. Singles, talk about your need for insurance.
   E. What two words should you say to your insurance agent if they do not have the heart of a teacher?   (Answer: YOU'RE FIRED!!!) Why?
   F. (Yes/No?) I have balanced my checkbook this month online or within 72 hours of receiving my bank statement. Why/Why not?
   G. Your FPU debit card holder has this warning on it: "Using this card may be hazardous to your financial health." Is this true? If you are using the card holder, has this subtle reminder helped you control your debit card spending?
   H. In what ways can having a debit card be almost as dangerous as a credit card?

III. Complete Insurance Coverage Recap sheet so that you will have all your insurance records in one place.   (See page 146)

• •

Member
RESOURCE CENTER
DaveRamsey.com/FPUMember

* Be sure to complete your homework the easy way online, and get great financial tools and resources for this week's lesson.
* Log in using your class code on page 22.

Insurance Coverage Recap

TYPE	COMPANY	PLAN ID #	POLICY #	AMOUNT	AGENT	PHONE #

Mortgage Information

TYPE	COMPANY	PHONE #	LOAN #	START	END	AMOUNT
1st						
2nd						

Dave Ramsey's
Financial Peace University

Retirement & College Planning

Travis Foster

"A good man leaves an inheritance for his children's children..."

Proverbs 13:22 (NIV)

Notes:

Retirement and College

Retirement and College

Disclaimer: This lesson is intended only for information! Because tax laws frequently change and various details have been omitted for the sake of time, you MUST check with your tax advisor to verify this information for your situation BEFORE you act.

Once the Emergency Fund is in place, you should begin retirement and college funding which all fall within long term investing for _____.

Baby Step 4: Invest 15% of household income into Roth IRAs and pre-tax retirement.

ALWAYS save long term with TAX - _____ dollars.

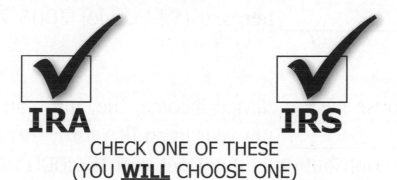

CHECK ONE OF THESE
(YOU **WILL** CHOOSE ONE)

Tax-favored means that the investment is in a _____ or has special tax treatment.

> *"Dishonest money dwindles away, but he who gathers money little by little makes it grow."*
>
> *Old Proverb*

Qualified Plans

- _____ _____ Account called an
  IRA, _____ Employee Pension Plan called a SEPP,
  _____ or _____ or _____
  or other deferred compensation plans.

Individual Retirement Accounts (IRA)

- Everyone with _____ income is eligible.

- Each person with earned income may have an IRA of up to
  $_____ per year ($4,000 for 2006-7, $5,000 begins
  2008).

- When a spouse has no earned income, they also can do
  $_____ per year in an IRA if the "working" spouse earns
  double the contribution amount per year ($4,000 for 2006-7,
  $5,000 begins 2008).

> **Remember**: IRA is not a _____ of
> investment at a bank. It is the tax treatment on virtually
> any type of investment.

Retirement and College

Roth IRA

Trivia: The Roth IRA is named for Senator William Roth (R-Delaware) who authored this section of the Taxpayer Relief Act of 1997.

The Roth IRA is an _____-tax IRA that grows TAX FREE!
If you save like we teach, you _____ use the Roth IRA.

Who is eligible?
- Singles
  100% contribution with income less than $95,000.
  Phase out between $95,000-$110,000. Not eligible above $110,000.
- Married filing jointly
  100% contribution with income less than $150,000.
  Phase out between $150,000-$160,000. Not eligible over $160,000.

Why the Roth IRA?

1) More _____.

2) Higher _____ at retirement.

3) More _____.

4) More _____.

Flexibility:
- Tax-free and penalty-free withdrawals anytime equal to contributions (after the emergency fund is depleted, you have a fall back).
- After five years tax-free, penalty-free withdrawals for 100% if:
  1) Over 59 and a half years old
  2) Because of death or disability
  3) First-time home purchase (max $10,000)

retirement and college

Simplified Employee Pension Plan (SEPP)

A _____-employed person may deduct up to _____ of their net profit on the business by investing in a SEPP.

The maximum deductible amount is $42,000 (as of 2005) and all employees who have been with the firm more than three of the last five years must receive the same percentage of their pay.

"Do not muzzle the ox while it is treading out the grain."
I Corinthians 9:9 (NIV)

401k, 403b & 457 Retirement Plans

_____ companies have completely done away with traditional pension plans in the last decade, according to Forbes. Some new plans offer a variety of pre-tax choices.

Do not use a Guaranteed Investment _____ (GIC) or bond funds to fund your plan.

You should be funding your plan whether your company matches or not, but the plans that have company matching provide_____ returns.

Retirement and College

Retirement and College

Rollovers

You should <u>always</u> roll all retirement plans to an IRA when you _____ the company.

> *When should you roll to the Roth IRA? You are not eligible to roll an IRA to a Roth if you are married and filing separately or if you have an income over $100,000.*

You should roll to a Roth IRA ONLY if:

1) You will have saved over _____ by age 65.

2) You pay your taxes _____, not from IRA.

3) You understand all taxes will become due on rollover amount.

Never _____ on your retirement plan.

If you are a federal government worker and have the standard thrift plan, we recommend _____ in the C Fund, _____ in the S Fund, and _____ in the I Fund.

Our Suggestion

Baby Step 4: Invest 15% of household income into Roth IRAs and pre-tax retirement.

1) Fund 401(k) or other employer plan if they match. Fund an _____ equal to the match.

2) Above the match amount, fund _____ IRAs. If there is no match, start with _____ IRAs.

3) Complete 15% of income by going to company _____ or SEPPs.

Note: This is the best plan if you end up with $700,000 or more by age 65 because mandatory retirement withdrawals will cause a higher tax bracket at retirement.

Retirement and College

Imagine if...

A 30-year-old couple fully funds a Roth IRA ($500 per month) at 12% interest. At 70 years old they will have . . .

$5,882,386.26 . . . TAX FREE!!!!

Imagine if...

That same 30-year-old couple made $40,000 and saved 15% in a 401(k) ($6,000.00 per year, $500.00 per month - at 12% interest). At 70 years old they will have . . .

$5,882,386.26 . . . in the 401(k)

By Retirement

That 30-year-old couple, DEBT FREE, saves $1,000 per month at 12% interest. At 70 years old, they will have:

Roth IRA	**$5,882,386.26**
401k	**$5,882,386.26**
Total	**$11,764,772.51**

...and to think this could be you.

College Planning

Baby Step 5: College Funding

Save for college first using Educational Saving Accounts (nicknamed "education _____").

You may save $2,000 per year, per child after tax that grows TAX FREE (of course we suggest growth mutual funds)!

Who is eligible?
- *Beneficiary must be under 18 years old.*
- *Must be used for higher education or tax and 10% penalty charged.*
- *Must be used or rolled to family member by age 30 or tax and 10% penalty charged.*
- *Singles contributing must make less than $95,000 income. Phase out between $95,000-$110,000. Not eligible above $110,000.*
- *Married filing jointly contributing must make less than $190,000. Phase out between $190,000-$220,000. Not eligible over $220,000 income.*

Above the ESA, you invest for college in good _____ stock mutual funds in an UTMA (or UGMA).

UTMA stands for Uniform _____ (or gift) to Minors Act.

- *The first $750 has zero tax.*
- *If the child is under 14 years old the next $750 is taxed at 10% or 15%. The rest is taxed at the parent's rate.*
- *If the child is over 14 years old, anything over $750 is taxed at child's bracket of 10% or 15%.*

Retirement and College

The account is _____ in the child's name and a
_____ is named, usually the parent or grandparent.
The _____ is the manager until the child reaches age 21.
At age 21 (age 18 for UGMA), they can do with it what they please.

So raise your kids right... Let the beatings begin.

> *"The rod and reproof give wisdom, but a child left to himself brings shame to his mother."*
>
> *Proverbs 29:15 (NKJV)*

Many states now offer _____ plans that allow for investment in mutual funds that grow tax-free for college.

The only 529 plans I would use are the ones that allow you to _____ your investment into certain mutual funds with long track records.

We do not recommend the age-based 529 plans because the returns are _____.

- *There is no income limit to do 529 investing, and you may place up to $10,000 per year per child into the plan.*

- *You may do more on a one time basis and all money put into the 529 plan is removed from your estate for estate tax planning.*

- *The money must be used for college or transferred to another beneficiary within the family, otherwise there will be a 10% penalty and taxes due.*

4 Nevers of College Saving

1. Never save for college using _____.

2. Never save for college using _____
   bonds. (Only 5-6%)

3. Never save for college using _____ _____
   bonds. (Only 6-8%)

4. Never save for college using _____
   college tuition. (Only 7% inflation rate)

Notes:

✓ Monthly College Planning

In order to have enough for college, you must aim at something. Your assignment is to determine how much per month you should be saving at 12% interest in order to have enough for college.

If we are saving at 12% and inflation is at 4%, then we are moving ahead of inflation at a net of 8% per year.

Step 1:

In today's dollars, how much per year does the college of your choice take:

$$\text{\$\underline{\qquad \$20,000 \qquad}}$$
$$\text{X 4 years} = \text{\$\underline{\qquad \$80,000 \qquad}}$$

(hint: $15,000 to $25,000 annually)

Step 2:

To achieve that college egg, you will save at 12% netting 8% after inflation, so we will target that college egg using 8%.

$80,000	X	.003287	=	$262.96
Nest Egg Needed		Factor		Monthly Savings Needed

8% Factors (select the one that matches your child's age)

CHILD'S AGE	YEARS TO SAVE	FACTOR
0	18	.002083
2	16	.002583
4	14	.003287
6	12	.004158
8	10	.005466
10	8	.007470
12	6	.010867
14	4	.017746

Note: Be sure to try one or two examples if you wait 5 or 10 years to start.

Retirement and College

Monthly College Planning

In order to have enough for college, you must aim at something. Your assignment is to determine how much per month you should be saving at 12% interest in order to have enough for college.

If we are saving at 12% and inflation is at 4%, then we are moving ahead of inflation at a net of 8% per year.

Step 1:

In today's dollars, how much per year does the college of your choice take:

$_____

X 4 years = $_____

(hint: $15,000 to $25,000 annually)

Step 2:

To achieve that college egg, you will save at 12% netting 8% after inflation, so we will target that college egg using 8%.

_____ X _____ = _____

Nest Egg Needed   Factor   Monthly Savings Needed

8% Factors (select the one that matches your child's age)

CHILD'S AGE	YEARS TO SAVE	FACTOR
0	18	.002083
2	16	.002583
4	14	.003287
6	12	.004158
8	10	.005466
10	8	.007470
12	6	.010867
14	4	.017746

Note: Be sure to try one or two examples if you wait 5 or 10 years to start.

Monthly Retirement Planning

In order to retire with some security, you must aim at something. Too many people use the READY-FIRE-AIM approach to retirement planning. Your assignment is to determine how much per month you should be saving at 12% interest in order to retire at 65 years old with what you need.

If we are saving at 12% and inflation is at 4%, then we are moving ahead of inflation at a net of 8% per year. If you invest your nest egg at retirement at 12% and want to break even with 4% inflation, you will be living on 8% income.

Step 1:

Annual Income (today) you wish to retire on: $30,000

divide by .08

(Nest egg needed)equals: $375,000

Step 2:

To achieve that nest egg you will save at 12% netting 8% after inflation so we will target that nest egg using 8%.

$375,000   X   .000436   = $163.50

Nest Egg Needed   Factor   Monthly Savings Needed

8% Factors (select the one that matches your age)

AGE	YEARS TO SAVE	FACTOR
25	40	.000286
30	35	.000436
35	30	.000671
40	25	.001051
45	20	.001698
50	15	.002890
55	10	.005466
60	5	.013610

Note: Be sure to try one or two examples if you wait 5 or 10 years to start.

Monthly Retirement Planning

In order to retire with some security, you must aim at something. Too many people use the READY-FIRE-AIM approach to retirement planning. Your assignment is to determine how much per month you should be saving at 12% interest in order to retire at 65 years old with what you need.

If we are saving at 12% and inflation is at 4%, then we are moving ahead of inflation at a net of 8% per year. If you invest your nest egg at retirement at 12% and want to break even with 4% inflation, you will be living on 8% income.

Step 1:

Annual Income (today) you wish to retire on: _____

divide by .08

(Nest egg needed)equals: _____

Step 2:

To achieve that nest egg you will save at 12% netting 8% after inflation so we will target that nest egg using 8%.

_____ X _____ = _____

Nest Egg Needed   Factor   Monthly Savings Needed

8% Factors (select the one that matches your age)

AGE	YEARS TO SAVE	FACTOR
25	40	.000286
30	35	.000436
35	30	.000671
40	25	.001051
45	20	.001698
50	15	.002890
55	10	.005466
60	5	.013610

Note: Be sure to try one or two examples if you wait 5 or 10 years to start.

retirement and college

✔ Retirement and College Planning

Answer Key (left to right)

Wealth	Favored	Qualified Plan
Individual	Retirement	Simplified
401K	403B	457
Earned	$3,000/$5000	$3,000/$5000
Type	After	Should
Choices	Bracket	Invested
Flexibility	Self	15%
Most	Contract	Great
Leave	$700,000	Separate
Borrow	40%	40%
20%	Amount	Roth
Roth	Plans	IRAs
Growth	Transfer	Listed
Custodian	Custodian	529
Freeze	Low	Insurance
Savings	Zero Coupon	Pre-paid

retirement and college

Retirement and College

Accountability Check-Up

Retirement & College Planning

I.   Review briefly (no more than 10 minutes) as a group the Monthly Retirement Planning worksheet.
   A.   If someone has a calculator, help each other figure out how much money you need to save to retire as you'd like to.
   B.   If you procrastinate and wait five to 10 years before getting started, calculate how much more you would have to save. *Note: These figures do not include any pre-existing savings towards retirement. If no one has a calculator, let everyone do it for homework themselves this week.

II.   Be prepared to name the Baby Steps, in order, at the next class session.

III. ACCOUNTABILITY & APPLICATION REVIEW: (Remember this is a support group; encourage one another.)
   A.   When you see retirement age people at the super stores, fast food, or a grocery store, does it ever make you stop and think, "That could be me some day!"? If so, does it emotionally motivate you to do something now about it? Should it? Why?
   B.   Should you ever TEMPORARILY stop adding to your retirement plan? If so, why? When should you start it up again?
   C.   Should you ever cash in pre-taxed retirement savings early to get out of debt? How would it affect your taxes?
   D.   Talk about how this lesson can make someone feel guilty or even depressed. How would you (How do you) feel if you were not ready financially for retirement?
   E.   Should you ever let your children's college funding get in the way of you building a proper foundation for your own financial future?
   F.   Why is it important to put aside three to six times your monthly expenses in an emergency fund and not three to six times your monthly income (according to Baby Step 3)?
   G.   Does college funding come before or after retirement savings according to the Baby Steps principles?   Why?
   H.   How does doing a monthly budget and living by it help you prepare for retirement?

retirement and college

· ·

* Be sure to complete your homework the easy way online, and get great financial tools and resources for this week's lesson.
* Log in using your class code on page 22.

Dave's tips for finding someone with

the *heart* *of a teacher*

retirement and college

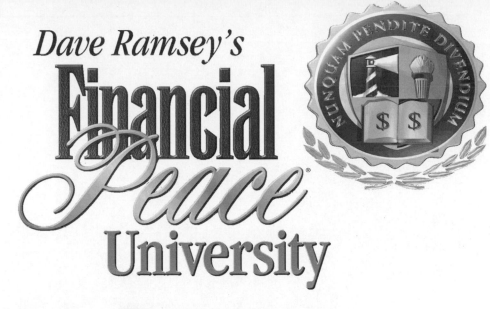

Dave Ramsey's
Financial Peace University

Buyer Beware

Travis Foster

"Almost any man knows how to earn money, but not one in a million knows how to spend it."

Henry David Thoreau

 **Notes:**

Buyer Beware

Buyer Beware – Caveat Emptor

Profile of the Enemy
(The enemy of your Financial Peace)

> *"He who has the most toys, wins, but he's still dead."*
>
> *Anonymous*

Companies use every angle to aggressively compete for your _Money_.

> *"The blessing of the Lord makes one rich, And He adds no sorrow with it."*
>
> *Proverbs 10:22 (NKJV)*

Four Major Ways are:

1. _Personally_ selling

2. _Financing_ as a marketing tool.

   - _78_% of 90 days same as cash contracts convert to payments which are usually at _24_% APR with Rule of 78's prepayment penalty.

3. _Television_, radio, and other _MEDIA_

4. Product _POSITIONING_

 Brand Recognition

 Shelf Position

 Color

 Packaging

Significant Purchases

A "Significant Purchase" is normally over $ _300_ .

Our body goes through physiological _CHANGES_ when making a "Significant Purchase."

What To Do

Because you can always spend more than you _MAKE_ , you must develop a POWER OVER _Purchase_ by:

1. Wait _over_ _Night_ before making a purchase.

> "He who is impulsive exalts folly."
>
> *Old Proverb*

2. Carefully consider your buying _Motives_ . (NEED/WANT)

> "In the house of the wise are stores of choice food and oil, but a foolish man devours all he has."
>
> *Proverbs 21:20 (NIV)*

No amount of _STUFF_ equals contentment or fulfillment.

> "For where your treasure is, there your heart will be also."
>
> *Matthew 6:21 (NKJV)*

3. Never buy anything you do not _UNDERSTAND_ .

> "A wise man will hear and increase in learning, and a man of understanding will acquire wise counsel."
>
> *Old Proverb*

4. Consider the "opportunity _Cost_ " of your money.

> "The plans of the diligent lead surely to plenty, but those of everyone who is hasty, surely to poverty."
>
> *Old Proverb*

5. Seek the _Counsel_ of your spouse.

> "Who can find a virtuous wife? For her worth is far above rubies. The heart of her husband safely trusts her: So he will have no lack of gain."
>
> *Proverbs 31:10-11 (NKJV)*

buyer beware

 **Discussion Questions**

1. How is financing used as a marketing tool?

2. Does packaging and advertising really affect your buying habits?

3. Someone give a personal example of "opportunity cost" of money.

4. Should you always have guilt or "conviction" when purchasing something "nice", and how do you know when that purchase is proper?

Answer Key (left to right)	
Money	Personal
Financing	78
24	TV
Media	Positioning
300	Changes
Make	Purchase
Over	Night
Motives	Stuff
Understand	Cost
Counsel	

buyer beware

✔ Accountability Check-Up

Buyer Beware

I. Check monthly budgets and see how everyone is doing.
    A. Are you truly trying to live by your budget?
    B. Are you making the necessary adjustment to fine-tune it?
    C. Plan on bringing next month's budget into class next week.
    D. Bring in your Financial Snapshot with column 3 completed next week.

II. Name the Baby Steps in order.

III. ACCOUNTABILITY & APPLICATION REVIEW: (Have each person answer and participate in this discussion.)
    A. I do not borrow money anymore, including on credit cards.
        True / False   Why or why not?
    B. I try to never pay retail for anything. (Share a recent bargain story with the class.)
    C. How have the Biblical principles of this program affected your view of handling personal finances?
    D. How would waiting overnight before making purchasing decisions have changed your debt load today? Talk about examples of things you've purchased impulsively in the past. Has this changed now for you?
    E. Do you seek the counsel of your spouse, if married, before making purchases over $300? If so, why? If not, why not? Should you?
    F. Whose counsel do you seek if you are single?
    G. Give an example of something you have bought in the past and did not fully understand how it worked. Would you do it again?
    H. In what ways has having an accountability partner been helpful to you? Do you still need help in this area?

IV. Everyone should show their Financial Snapshot with Column 3 completed.
    A. Invite class members to share a victory story with the class as you reflect on your progress throughout this program.

● ●

* Be sure to complete your financial snapshot and homework the easy way online, and get great financial tools and resources for this week's lesson.
* Log in using your class code on page 22.

Do You Have A Powerful Testimony That You Would Like To Share With Us About How FPU Has Touched Your Life?

Please Share It With Us!

Visit **www.daveramsey.com/fpu/home**
and look for this link:

Or Mail, Fax, E-mail
It To Our Office At:

Mail -
1749 Mallory Lane, Suite 100
Brentwood, TN 37027

Fax -
1-615-371-5007

E-mail -
fpu@daveramsey.com

Dave Ramsey's

Financial *Peace*® University

Real Estate & Mortgages

Travis Foster

"Prepare your outside work, make it fit for yourself in the field; and afterward build your house."

Proverbs 24:27 (NKJV)

Notes:

Real Estate & Mortgages

Selling a Home

When selling a home, you should think like a _BUYER_.

The home should be in "near perfect" condition.

The return on investment of fix-up dollars is _____.

Paint, lawn care, wallpaper, etc. make a home sell faster and for more money. So DO IT!!!

The most important aspect of preparation is attention to the _____ appeal.

> *"You never get a second chance to make a good first impression."*
> *Zig Ziglar*

When selling your home, statistical research has found that the best Realtors are worth _More_ than they cost, unless you are a seasoned pro.

The exposure through the _Multiple_ Listing Service is worth it.

When selecting a Realtor, do _Not_ rely on friendships or relatives.

You should _Interview_ at least 3 Realtors.

Offering a home warranty typically will _Not_ make a sale. If the buyer asks for a warranty, then consider it with that offer.

> *"A man builds a fine house; and now he has a master, and a task for life; he is to furnish, watch, show it, and keep it in repair the rest of his days."*
>
> *Ralph Waldo Emerson*

Buying a Home

Home ownership is a great investment for three main reasons.

1) ___*Forced*___ Savings Plan

2) ___*INFLATION*___ Hedge

3) Grows virtually tax *Free* . (You can have a gain of $250,000 single or $500,000 married and pay zero tax on your personal residence if you hold it at least two years.)

→ Always Buy

Title insurance insures you against an ___*UNCLEAN*___ title, which is when your proper ownership is in question. It is a good buy.

Always get a land survey if buying more than a standard subdivision ___*LOT*___.

Realtors' access to the ___*MLS*___ system can make house hunting easier, BUT they think like a retailer.

Real Estate & Mortgages

What to Buy

Bottom of price range in the _Bottom NEIGHBORHOOD_.

Homes appreciate in good neighborhoods and are priced based on three things: _Location_, _Location_, & _Location_.

If possible, buy near _WATER_ or with a _VIEW_.

Buy bargains by overlooking bad landscaping, ugly carpet, ugly wallpaper, and the _Elvis_ print in the master bedroom;

BUT

Always buy a home that is (or can be) attractive from the _Street_ and that has a good basic _floor_ plan.

> *"Any structural weirdness you are willing to overlook will cost you at resale."*
>
> *Anonymous*

Have the home inspected mechanically and structurally by a certified _Home Inspector_.

Appraisals are an "_Opinion_ of value" but a better opinion than the seller's, so order one if in doubt.

Mortgages

First, remember to ___*HATE*___ debt.

The best mortgage is the ___*100%*___ down plan.

> *"There are also some who said, 'we have mortgaged our lands and vineyards and houses, that we might buy grain because of the famine'."*
>
> *Nehemiah 5:3 (NKJV)*

But if you must...

Then try something radical, like really believing that less home will do for a while.

Get a payment of no more than ___*25%*___ of take home pay on a

___*15 yr*___ fixed rate loan, with at least ___*10%*___ down. Have a fully

funded emergency fund left over after closing.

Real Estate & Mortgages

TO BUY?
OR WHAT TO BUY?
THAT IS THE QUESTION

(FIGURES BASED ON 8% APR)

I. **$95,000**   **15-years Pay $907/mo**

II. **$95,000**   **30-years Pay $697/mo**
                                          $210/mo

BUT AFTER TEN YEARS...

The 15-year loan has a balance of $44,000 while the 30-year loan has a balance of $83,000!!!!

During that 10 years you paid more than $83,600 but only paid down the loan by less than $12,000.

That is why it is good to own a bank!

Adjustable Rate Mortgages (ARMS) were brought on with the advent of ___HIGH___ interest rates in the early 1980's.

The concept of the ARM is to ___TRANSFER___ the risk of higher interest rates to the ___Borrow___, and in return the lender gives a lower rate now.

According to the FDIC, more than ___35___% of ARMs are adjusted inaccurately, so check yours if you have one.

You can qualify for more home with ARMs, but the risk of financial stress later is not worth it.

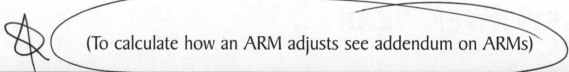

(To calculate how an ARM adjusts see addendum on ARMs)

> *"For which of you, intending to build a tower, does not sit down first and count the cost, whether he has enough to finish it lest, after he has laid the foundation, and is not able to finish it, all who see it begin to mock him, saying 'This man began to build and was not able to finish.'"*
>
> *Luke 14:28-30 (NKJV)*

Real Estate & Mortgages

Basic Ways to Finance a Home

1. _____CONVENTIONAL_____ usually through FNMA and insured against default privately.

   Down payments range from 5% to 20% or more.

   These loans are available in all forms and formats.

   With 20% down or 20% LTV you can save PMI.

   PMI is _____PRIVATE_____ mortgage insurance. $70/$100,000

2. _____FHA_____ which is insured by HUD-the federal government.

   FHA charges a <u>Mortgage Insurance Premium (MIP)</u> that <u>never drops off</u> no matter how far down you pay the loan.

   Down payments are as low as ___3___% and are used on lower priced homes.

   These loans are currently _____More_____ expensive than conventional financing and should be avoided.

3.   _____VA_____ which is insured by the Veterans Administration.

Designed to benefit the veteran; the seller pays everything allowing a true zero-down purchase.

With a good down payment, the conventional loan is a _____BETTER_____ deal.

4.   _____OWNER_____ financing is when you pay the owner over time, making him the mortgage holder.

This is a _____GREAT_____ way to finance because you can be creative in the structure of the loan.

Example: No payments for a year, interest rates that graduate, or discount for early payoff.

Real Estate & Mortgages

Addendum One

How to Figure Your New Payment
Monthly Payment per $1,000 in Loan Amount

Rate	15-Year	30-Year
4.5%	7.65	5.07
5.0%	7.91	5.37
5.5%	8.17	5.68
6.0%	8.44	6.00
6.5%	8.71	6.32
7.0%	8.99	6.66
7.5%	9.28	7.00
8.0%	9.56	7.34
8.5%	9.85	7.69
9.0%	10.15	8.05
9.5%	10.44	8.41
10.0%	10.75	8.78
10.5%	11.05	9.15
11.0%	11.37	9.52
11.5%	11.68	9.90
12.0%	12.00	10.29

_____ / 1,000 = _____ X _____ = _____

Sales Price / 1,000 = #1000's   X   Factor   = Monthly Pymt

Example: Sales Price - $90,000, 15 years at 8%

$90,000 / 1,000 = 90 X 9.56 (look at rate and # of years financed) =

$860.40 Monthly Payment

Addendum Two

Should I Refinance?

Current principal and interest payment
(not with taxes & insurance)   _____

New principal and interest payment (minus)   _____
Equals monthly savings   _____

_____ / _____ = _____

Total closing costs divided by savings = number of months to break even

Example: Refinance on a $90,000 mortgage

$1,100 current payment - $950 new payment = $150 savings
$1,950 closing cost divided by $150 savings = 13 months

Will you stay in your home longer than the number of months to break even? If so, you are a candidate for a refinance.

ESTIMATED CLOSING COSTS TABLE

Loan Amount	Closing Costs	Loan Amount	Closing Costs
30,000	1,500	35,000	1,550
40,000	1,600	45,000	1,650
50,000	1,700	55,000	1,725
60,000	1,775	65,000	1,800
70,000	1,825	75,000	1,850
80,000	1,900	85,000	1,925
90,000	1,950	95,000	1,975
100,000	2,000	150,000	2,300
200,000	2,600	250,000	2,900

real estate & mortgages

Real Estate & Mortgages

Addendum Three

How To Figure The Change In Your ARM

Your Adjustable Rate Mortgage adjusts based on the movement of an index. You can find your index in your original note or mortgage. The most commonly used index is the Treasury Bill. The one-year ARM uses the one-year T-Bill, and the three-year ARM uses the three-year T-Bill and so on. Other commonly used indexes are the LIBOR and the 11TH DISTRICT COST OF FUNDS.

First, find out what index you use and when it is adjusted.

Next, find out (also from your paperwork) what margin was assigned to your loan (usually 2.59).

Basically your ARM moves as the index moves.

The index is usually published daily in the *Wall Street Journal.*

So if you have a one-year ARM that adjusts with the one-year T-Bill and a margin of 2.59 (which is typical), then at the one-year anniversary of your closing you would look up the one-year T-Bill in the *Wall Street Journal.* Add the T-Bill to your margin and you have your new rate (if it is not capped).

Example: T-Bill 4.41 plus margin 2.59 = 7% new interest rate.

Warning: Almost all ARMs start below margin the first year, guaranteeing a payment increase at anniversary unless rates DROP.

✔ Discussion Questions

1. How important is home ownership? Why?

2. Are there times when you should not own?

3. How can you prevent becoming "house poor"?

<u>Answer Key</u> (left to right)

Retailer	Enormous	Curb	More
Multiple	Not	Interview	Not
Forced	Inflation	Free	Unclean
Lot	MLS	Neighborhood	Location
Location	Location	Water	View
Elvis	Street	Floor	Home
Inspector	Opinion	Hate	100%
25%	15-year	10%	High
Transfer	Borrower	35	Conventional
Private	FHA	3	More
VA	Better	Owner	Great

Real Estate & Mortgages

 **Accountability Check-Up**

Real Estate & Mortgages

I.   BUDGET CHECK TIME AGAIN!
  A. This should be around your third monthly zero-based budget during this 13-week program.
  B. By now everyone should start to have a better handle on how to do a budget and their average monthly spending.
  C. As a result you should feel a little bit more in control of your finances. If you still need more help call The Lampo Group office at 1-888-22PEACE for more assistance or information regarding a 1-2 hour phone counseling session.

II. ACCOUNTABILITY & APPLICATION REVIEW:
  A. If you find yourself paying more on a house than you can realistically afford, what should you do? Talk about the struggle this has or would cause you.
  B. How can renting for a period of time actually be wise in the big financial picture? Is renting for a time really throwing away money?
  C. Have you ever been late on a mortgage or rent payment? If so, how did it make you feel?
  D. If you have over a 15-year mortgage, make a commitment to at least look into how much interest you would save by switching it to a 15-year or less mortgage.
  E. If you have an ARM (Adjustable Rate Mortgage), should you look into moving it to a fixed rate? Why or why not? If anyone in the class has ever had an ARM and it hurt them financially, share the history with the class.
  F. How would paying off your house early feel? How would it affect your retirement?
  G. Complete this sentence: "This program has been a blessing in my life because it has…"

III. Let The Lampo Group know what FPU means to you. E-mail us at fpu@daveramsey.com or call us at 1-888-22PEACE.

* Be sure to complete your homework the easy way online, and get great financial tools and resources for this week's lesson.
* Log in using your class code on page 22.

real estate & mortgages

real estate & mortgages

Dave Ramsey's
Financial Peace University

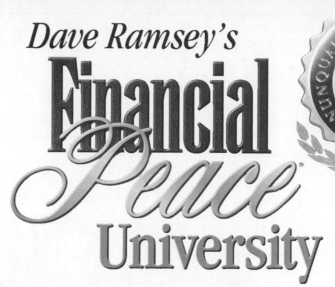

Careers & Extra Jobs

Travis Foster

"How long will you slumber, O sluggard? When will you rise from your sleep? A little sleep, a little slumber, a little folding of the hands to sleep... So shall your poverty come on you like a robber..."

Proverbs 6:9-11

Careers & Extra Jobs

✓ Business Employment Trends

National Firms by Employment Size

0-4 employees................59.3%

5-9 employees................19.2%

10-19 employees...........11.6%

20-49 employees............6.6%

50-99 employees............2.0%

100-449 employees.......1.42%

500-999 employees.......0.28%

Census Bureau Statistics

Dealing With Change

- The average job in America is now _____3.2_____ years in length.

- The average American worker will have _16–18_ ~Positions~ different jobs in his/her working lifetime.

- We know this about college graduates: Ten years after graduation, _____80%_____ of college graduates are working in something totally unrelated to their college degree.

- Experts tell us that _____85%_____ of all products and services we are now using will be obsolete in five years.

Careers & Extra Jobs

> *"Everyone lives on the edge of job obsolescence and on the threshold of career opportunity."*
>
> *Anonymous*

The key to power in our careers is to first look at _ourselves_.

The more we understand ourselves, the more we can move forward with boldness and confidence. We can enhance our effectiveness by first being introspective.

> *"Know thyself, and to thine own self be true."*
>
> *Shakespeare*

> *"The unexamined life is not worth living."*
>
> *Socrates*

> *"The secret of success is focus of purpose."*
>
> *Thomas Edison*

Money is ultimately never enough compensation for doing a job.

There must be a sense of _MEANING_, _Purpose_, and _Accomplishment_.

Just because you have the _ABILITY_ to do something does not mean that it is well-suited for you.

Any job you have must blend your:

Skills and _Abilitie_

Pesonalty _Traits_

Values, _Dream_ and _Passions_

The real goal is to:

PLAN YOUR WORK AROUND YOUR LIFE RATHER THAN PLANNING YOUR LIFE AROUND YOUR WORK.

Careers & Extra Jobs

Understanding My Personal Characteristics

Recognize that your _____*Job*_____ is not your LIFE. It is simply one tool for a successful life.

Learn to distinguish between the following terms:

- Your _____*Vocation*_____ is a calling, purpose, mission and destiny.

> *There is a Hebrew word "Avodah" from which come both the words "work" and "worship". To the Hebrew man, what he was doing on Thursday morning was just as much an expression of worship as being in the synagogue on the Sabbath.*

> *The master in the art of living makes little distinction between his work and his play, his labor and his leisure, his mind and his body, his information and his recreation, his love and his religion. He hardly knows which is which. He simply pursues his vision of excellence at whatever he does, leaving others to decide whether he is working or playing. To him, he is always doing both.*
>
> *James Michener*

- Your _____*Career*_____ is a line of work but not necessarily your calling.

- Your _____*Job*_____ is your daily activity that produces an income or paycheck.

The major quest in life is not what you ___are___ ___Gettig___ but what you ___are___ ___becoming___ .

Understanding your ___Personal___ style will tell you more about where you will function successfully than knowing your ___Educational___ background.

A recent Harvard University study reported that ___15%___ of the reason for a person's success is due to technical skill and knowledge. ___85%___ of the reason originates from that person's personal skill, attitude, enthusiasm, self-discipline, desire, and ambition.

This is why candidates with the best ___Qualifications___ on paper frequently do not get the job.

> *In* **The Millionaire Mind,** *a study of decamillionaires, Dr. Thomas Stanley reports that a direct correlation could not be found between academic background, or even IQ, and success. The only common theme among those who end up very wealthy is that they find something they love and do it with excellence.*

Resumes

Remember, resumes get you ___Interviews___ . Interviews get you jobs.

> *"The measure of a man is not what he does on Sunday, but rather who is is Monday through Saturday."*
>
> *Anonymous*

Interviews

Most hiring decisions are made in the first _3_ to _5_ minutes of an interview.

Consequently, we know that the interviewer is responding more to personal qualities than to resume qualifications.

> *"The major difference between successful and unsuccessful job hunters is not skill, education, or ability, but the way they go about their job hunt."*
>
> *Anonymous*

Job Search Strategy

Ads in the paper represent about _15%_ of what is available. Go after the other 85% as well.

Responding to ads in the paper leads to jobs for about 15 out of 100 job seekers.

Employment agencies lead to success for about 13 out of 100. The proper job search strategy leads to a job for 86 out of 100 who use it.

Target the companies for which you would like to work and contact them at least three times.

1. _Introduction_ _Letter_
2. _Cover_ _letter_ and _Resume_
3. _Phone_ _Follow-Up_

Taking an active approach for _30_ - _45_ days will open up opportunities that you desire.

> *"Ask, 'How can I make my ideas profitable?'"*
>
> *Anonymous*

Supplemental Income

Long term income changes are covered by career changes, but many times the best way to meet short term _OBJECTIVES_ is to take the dreaded _Part_ - _Time_ job.

The following are examples of short term objectives:

1. Eliminate _Monthly_ bills.

2. _Pay-off_ debt.

3. _Purchase_ an item with cash.

4. Build up _Lump_ sum savings.
   (College or Emergency Fund)

Home-based businesses are another method of generating supplemental income.

*Forty-five percent of American homes have a business within its walls,...

Entrepreneur Magazine

Careers & Extra Jobs

Ideas of Successful Home-Based Businesses

Accounting	Wedding Planning
Personal Service	Senior Citizen Care
Appliance Repair	Graphic Design
Gift Baskets	Newsletters
Vending	Delivery Service
Interior Decorating	Flea Market Vendor
Landscape Design	Home Inspection
Window Displaying	Ceiling Fans
House Painting	Auto Detailing
Consignment Used Cars	Glass Tinting
Child Security Systems	Power Washing
One-Person Entertainer	Catering
Nutrition Counselor	Wild Herbs
Organic Gardening	Jewelry Sales
Tree Removal	Chimney Cleaning
Glass Etching	Firewood Supply
Kitchen Tune-ups	Decks & Coverings
Home Schooling Counselor	Manners Instruction
Mail Order	Balloon Vendor
Pet Sitter	Real Estate Photos
Aerial Photos	Discount Coupon
Books	Web Designer
Marketing	How-To-Brochures
Sewing Alterations	Tour Guide
College Scholarship Search	Computer Consultant
Electroplating	Import/Export Broker

In Conclusion: WARNING

Beware! Do not allow your work (career) to be the source of all your satisfaction and self ___WORTH___ .

> *"Do not overwork to be rich; Because of your own understanding, cease! Will you set your eyes on that which is not? For riches certainly make themselves wings; They fly away like an eagle toward heaven."*
>
> *Proverbs 23:4-5 (NKJV)*

> *"If you want to know how rich you really are, find out what would be left of your tomorrow if you should lose every dollar you own tonight."*
>
> *William J. Boetcher*

> *"Career is a means to an end, not the end."*
>
> *Anonymous*

> *"Think beyond your lifetime if you want to accomplish something truly worthwhile."*
>
> *Walt Disney*

"Have Time" Book to read

Careers & Extra Jobs

Personal Mission Statement Worksheet

Skills and Interests: _____

_____

_____

Personality Traits: _____

_____

_____

Values, Dreams, and Passions: _____

_____

MY MISSION IS: _____

_____

_____

> *"Outstanding people have one thing in common: an absolute sense of mission."*
>
> *Anonymous*

Examples of a Mission Statement

I will maintain a positive attitude and a sense of humor in everything I do. I want to be known by my family as a caring and loving husband and father; by my business associates as a fair and honest person; and my friends as someone they can count on to earn their respect. Controlling all my actions is a strong sense of integrity which I believe is the most important character trait.

My Mission is to provide service, products, and benefits with integrity and honesty to the medical community. I will look for opportunities to help hurting individuals and assist other professionals in a win-win manner. I will not knowingly harm or take advantage of anyone. I will use my knowledge and abilities in organizing and structuring in ways that provide income and pleasure for my family and blessings to those around me.

My Mission is to exercise my creativity and innovative ideas by developing songs, books and products which change lives and society for the better. I will use my talents and abilities consistently. I will not hide them simply because they will not always be immediately recognized. I want all of my work to be a product of God's inspiration and a blessing to the world. I will be loyal to my family, friends and God.

For myself, I want to develop self-knowledge, self-love, and self-allowing. I want to use my healing talents to keep hope alive and express my vision courageously in work and action. In my family, I want to build healthy, loving relationships in which we let each other become our best selves. At work, I want to establish a fault-free, self-perpetuating, learning environment. In the world, I want to nurture the development of all life forms, in harmony with the laws of nature.

Careers & Extra Jobs

Personality Inventory

Instructions: In each box, circle each word or phrase that describes a consistent character trait of yours. You should find groupings in 1 or 2 categories. Then turn to the next page for corresponding career areas.

Dominance (Driver)

Likes Authority
Takes Charge
Controlling
Bold
Decision Maker
Enterprising
Task Oriented
Overlooks Details
Not careful of Other's Feelings
Adventurous
Determined
Self-reliant
Independent
Confident
Very Direct

Influencing (Expressive)

Enthusiastic
Visionary
Takes Risks
Spontaneous
Enjoys Change
Group Oriented
Likes Variety
Creative New Ideas
Optimistic
Infectious Laughter
Inspirational
Initiator
Promoter
Can Waste Time
Entertains Others

Steadiness (Amiable)

Calm
Loyal
Nurturing
Dry Humor
Sympathetic
Conscientious
Peace Maker
Enjoys Routine
Understanding
Avoids Conflict
Dislikes Change
Maintains Low Profile
Can Be Slow to Act
Good Listener
Reliable

Compliance (Analytical)

Predictable
Controlled
Perfectionist
Diplomatic
Inquisitive
Accurate
Orderly
Factual
Loves Detail
Conscientious
Reserved
Discerning
Precise
Scheduled
Sensitive

Occupational Categories

In the boxes below are some of the occupations that line up with the personal characteristics you checked on the previous page. These are broad categories, but will give you an idea of what would be most fitting for you. This is not a complete list, but will give you an idea of how types of jobs use the same personal skills.

Dominance

Manufacturer's Representative
Lobbyist
Business Manager
Fire Marshall
Travel Guide
Principal
Fashion Coordinator
Landscape Architect
Sales Agent, Insurance
Production Coordinator
Show Host/Hostess
Manager, Customer Services
Sales Agent, Real Estate
Announcer
Writer
Entrepreneur
Business Owner

Influencing

Training Representative
Clergy Member
Manager, Advertising
Editor
Preschool Teacher
Arbitrator
Sales Agent
Administrator, Health Care
Home Economist
Actor/Actress
Reporter
Manager, Office
Insurance Sales
Optometrist
Illustrator
Faculty Member
Interior Designer

Steadiness

Investigator
Pharmacist
Physical Instructor
Psychologist
Survey Worker
Counselor
Social Worker
Teacher, Secondary School
Correspondence Clerk
Market Research Analyst
Veterinarian
Nurse
Podiatrist
Programmer
Lab Technician
Chiropractor
Librarian

Compliance

Medical Record Technician
Nurse, Licensed Practical
Nurse, General Duty
Secretary
Accountant
Job Analyst
Mail Clerk
Caseworker
Architect
Biochemist
District Ext. Service Agent
Geologist
Physical Assistant
Historian
Environmental Analyst
Airplane Pilot
Painter

Careers & Extra Jobs

I Do Not Choose To Be A Common Man

It is my right to be uncommon — If I can.

I seek opportunity — not security. I do not wish to be a kept citizen, humbled and dulled by having the state look after me.

I want to take the calculated risk; to dream and to build, to fail and to succeed.

I refuse to barter incentive for a dole. I prefer the challenges of life to the guaranteed existence; the thrill of fulfillment to the stale calm of utopia.

I will not trade freedom for beneficence nor my dignity for a handout. I will never cower before any master nor bend to any threat.

It is my heritage to stand erect, proud and unafraid; to think and act for myself, enjoy the benefit of my creations and to face the world boldly and say, This I have done.

By Dean Alfange

All this is what it means to be an American.

Discussion Questions

1. Do you have family, career, spiritual, physical and personal development goals as well as financial goals?

2. Discuss the fit of your job with your personality style.

3. Discuss resumes, interviews and networking.

4. What ideas do you have for a home-based business?

<u>Answer Key</u> (left to right)		
3.2	16 - 18	80%
85%	Ourselves	Money
Meaning	Purpose	Accomplishment
Ability	Skills	Abilities
Personality	Traits	Values
Dreams	Passions	Job
Vocation	Career	Job
Are	Getting	Are
Becoming	Personal	Educational
15%	85%	Qualification
Interviews	3	5
15%	Introduction	Letter
Cover	Letter	Resume
Phone	Follow-up	30
45	Objectives	Part
Time	Monthly	Pay off
Purchase	Lump	Worth

✔ Accountability Check-Up

Careers & Extra Jobs

I.   As you cut up credit cards again, tally how much debt the class has avoided by not accepting any new credit card offers.
   A. Add up the credit limits on credit card applications the group has received over the last few months.
   B. Have a credit card and application destroying party.
   C. Congratulate each other for avoiding any new debt.
   D. You've worked hard for your money! It's time to be FREED!

II. ACCOUNTABILITY & APPLICATION REVIEW:
   (Talk with passion about these things.)
   A. How can having a personal mission statement affect your life? Do you feel it's important enough to write it out and display it?
   B. Describe the feelings of working at a job where you feel stuck because of financial responsibilities, yet for which you have no passion.
   C. Discuss some of the benefits to working a second job (temporarily) to pay off debts with gazelle intensity.
   D. Do you believe you are doing your life's work? Do you have the kind of job that brings happiness and inner peace? If not, why?
   E. Talk about the emotional stress that you might go through if you were out of work for a long period of time.
   F. Answer to yourself: (True or False) I am supportive of my spouse's work and encourage him/her for all the hard work he/she does to help provide for the family.
   G. Talk about the danger of being a workaholic. How can it affect your life, your soul, and your family? Does it become a non-issue if you are single?
   H. How can having a job you enjoy make a difference in your financial future?
   I. Talk about why it is harder to pay off debts when you are working at a job that you do not enjoy.
   J. Colossians 3:23 teaches us that "...whatever you do, do it heartily, as to the Lord and not to men." Do you carry this attitude into your workplace? How could it help you even if you are working at a job you don't enjoy?

IV. Go home and finish the Personality Inventory and Occupational Categories worksheets this week.

V.   Work on your Personal Mission Statement worksheet this week!

• •

* Be sure to complete your homework the easy way online, and get great financial tools and resources for this week's lesson.
* Log in using your class code on page 22.

careers & extra jobs

Be Sure to Check the Web for the NEW Release of FPU Online!

As an FPU Member, you can review any lesson online at a discounted rate.

Just visit
www.daveramsey.com/fpu/home
for more information

Dave Ramsey's
Financial Peace University

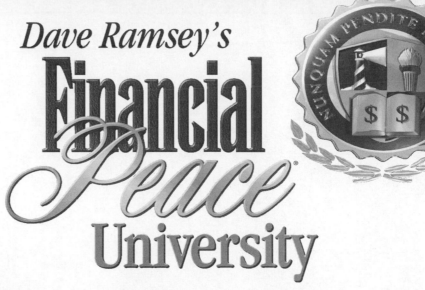

Collection Practices & Credit Bureaus

Travis Foster

"Do not withhold good from those to whom it is due, when it is in the power of your hand to do so. Do not say to your neighbor, 'Go, and come back, and tomorrow I will give it,' when you have it with you."

Proverbs 3:27-28 (NKJV)

 **Notes:**

Collection Practices

Collection Practices

Collection Practices

The best way to pay debts is with a _____.

> *"There is no dignity quite so impressive, and no independence quite so important, as living within your means."*
>
> *Calvin Coolidge*

> *"Many are the plans in a man's heart, But the counsel of the LORD, it will stand."*
>
> *Proverbs 19:21 (NASB)*

A collector's job is not to help your overall situation but to get _____ money only.

Collectors are trained _____ _____ or _____.

They are typically low-paid positions with high _____.

They are taught in their training to evoke strong _____.

The way you counteract this technique is to ALWAYS pay necessities first, and then _____ set the order of payment.

In 1977, a consumer law was passed by Congress called the Federal Fair Debt Collection Practices Act to protect you from unfair collectors. The law technically only applies to collection agencies (not your creditor), but later court cases make most creditors also abide by the FFDCPA.

The Act states that harassment is illegal, and that includes restricting a collector's calls between the hours of _____ and _____ (unless they have your permission).

The Act also allows you to demand a creditor cease calling you at _____. You should request this in writing by certified mail return receipt requested. (See sample letter)

The Act even allows you to insist a creditor stop ALL contact _____ to notify you of lawsuit proceedings.

> *"I've never been poor, only broke. Being poor is a frame of mind. Being broke is only a temporary position."*
>
> *Mike Todd*

Collection Practices

Do not use a cease and desist letter except in _____ situations because all negotiations stop and any hope of a positive resolution is lost.

> *"A good name is to be chosen rather than great riches, loving favor rather than silver and gold."*
>
> *Old Proverb*

No collector or creditor may confiscate a _____ account or garnishee (attach) _____ without proper and lengthy court action. All such threats are a bluff.

Your plan should include as much prompt repayment of debt as possible in order to protect your credit rating, but YOU must set your priorities of repayment. Do NOT let a collector use your credit report as a _____ club.

> *"It is better not to vow than to vow and not pay."*
>
> *Ecclesiastes 5:5 (NKJV)*

> *"A light purse is a heavy curse."*
>
> *Benjamin Franklin*

When you are unable to pay the minimum payments, use the _____ _____ plan.

Pro Rata Debts

Discover	$1,200	$150
Citibank Visa	300	45
MBNA Visa	200	25
Penny's	100	60
Sears	200	30
TOTAL	$2,000	$310

Income	$2,400
Necessity Expense	- 2,200
Disposable Income	$ 200

Can't increase income anytime soon

Pro Rata Plan

Sheet 11

ITEM	TOTAL PAYOFF	TOTAL /DEBT	= PERCENT	DISPOSABLE X INCOME	NEW = PAYMENTS
Discover	1,200	/ 2000	= .60	X 200	= 120
Citibank	300	/ 2000	= .15	X 200	= 30
MBNA	200	/ 2000	= .10	X 200	= 20
Penny's	100	/ 2000	= .05	X 200	= 10
Sears	200	/ 2000	= .10	X 200	= 20

Collection Practices

collection practices

Pro Rata Debts

Sheet 11

If you cannot pay your creditors what they request, you should treat them all fairly and the same. You should pay even the ones who are not jerks and pay everyone as much as you can. Many creditors will accept a written plan and cut special deals with you as long as you are communicating, maybe even over communicating, and sending them something. We have had clients use this even when sending only $2 and have survived for literally years.

Pro rata means their share or what percent of your total debt they represent. That will determine how much you send them. You should send the check with a budget and this sheet attached each month, even if the creditor says they will not accept it.

ITEM	TOTAL PAYOFF	TOTAL /DEBT	= PERCENT	DISPOSABLE x INCOME	NEW = PAYMENTS
_____	_____	/ _____	= . _____	X _____	= _____
_____	_____	/ _____	= . _____	X _____	= _____
_____	_____	/ _____	= . _____	X _____	= _____
_____	_____	/ _____	= . _____	X _____	= _____
_____	_____	/ _____	= . _____	X _____	= _____
_____	_____	/ _____	= . _____	X _____	= _____
_____	_____	/ _____	= . _____	X _____	= _____
_____	_____	/ _____	= . _____	X _____	= _____
_____	_____	/ _____	= . _____	X _____	= _____
_____	_____	/ _____	= . _____	X _____	= _____
_____	_____	/ _____	= . _____	X _____	= _____
_____	_____	/ _____	= . _____	X _____	= _____
_____	_____	/ _____	= . _____	X _____	= _____
_____	_____	/ _____	= . _____	X _____	= _____
_____	_____	/ _____	= . _____	X _____	= _____

Pro Rata Sample Letter

Date: Feb. 22, 2006

From: Joe and Suzie Public
     123 Anystreet
     Anytown, ST 11111

To: Mega Credit Card Company
    999 Main Street
    Big City, ST 00000

Re: Joe and Suzie Public # 1234-5678-9012-9999

Dear Collection Manager:

Recently I lost my job, and my wife is employed in a clerical position. We have met with a financial counselor to assess our present situation.

We acknowledge our indebtedness to you of $6,000 and fully intend to pay you back in full. However, you are one of six creditors to whom we owe $42,968. We owe minimum payments of $782 each month. We are not able to meet these minimum payments at the present time, and we are not planning on going into further debt to meet these obligations.

We have put together a basic necessities cash flow plan based on our take-home pay of $2,340 per month (see the enclosed copy of cash flow plan). Since we have two small children and no disposable income currently to pay our creditors, we can not make a payment to you at the present time, but we do not intend to go bankrupt.

Consequently, we are asking for a moratorium on payments for the next 120 days. We will keep in close contact with you, and as soon as possible, we will begin making payments. If possible, we would like to request a reduction on interest during this time.

We are aware that this is an inconvenience to you, but we must meet the basic needs of our family first. We fully intend to pay our creditors all that we owe them. Please be patient with us. If you have any questions please contact us at 600-555-9876.

Thank you for your consideration of our present situation.

Sincerely,

Joe Public
Suzie Public

# ✔ Pro Rata Plan Letter

Date: _____

From: _____

_____

_____

To: Name of Creditor
    Address

Re: Card holder name and account number

Dear: (If you know a specific person or, when contacting them by phone, get name of area or office supervisor.)

Recently (I have had to..........................) Or (my husband had......................) changed jobs and have met with a financial counselor to assess our present situation.

We acknowledge our indebtedness to you of $_____, and fully intend to pay you back in full. However, you are one of _____ creditors to whom we owe $_____. We owe minimum payments of $ _____ each month. We are not able to meet these minimum payments at the present time, and we are not planning on going into further debt to meet these obligations.

We have put together a basic necessities cash flow plan based on our take-home pay of $_____ per month (enclose copy of cash flow plan). Since we have _____ small children and no (or limited) disposable income currently to pay our creditors, we (can or cannot) make a payment to you (of $_____) at the present time, but we do not intend to go bankrupt.

Consequently, we are asking for a moratorium on payments for the next _____(30, 60, 90, or 120) days. We will keep in close contact with you, and as soon as possible, we will begin making payments. If possible, we would like to request a reduction on interest during this time.

We are aware that this is an inconvenience to you, but we must meet the basic needs of our family first. We fully intend to pay our creditors all that we owe them. Please be patient with us. If you have any questions please contact us at _____ (phone number).

Thank you for your consideration of our present situation.

Sincerely,
(Signatures)

Eventually, if you are making no payments and have cut no deals, you will get sued.

> *"And if anyone wants to sue you, and take your shirt, let him have your coat also. And whoever shall force you to go one mile, go with him two. Give to him who asks of you, and do not turn away from him who wants to borrow from you."*
>
> *Matthew 5:40-42 (NASB)*

Typically lawsuits for under _____ are sued in General Sessions Court (or small claims court) which is a fairly informal proceeding.

Before you are sued, you will be served by the local sheriff's department and given typically _____ days notice of the court date.

In court, if the debt is valid, even if you fight, you will lose. From that date you will have _____ days before the judgement becomes final and garnishments or attachments begin.

At ANY TIME during the process, you may settle with the creditor or their attorney in writing. If you are not able to reach agreement, you can file with the court a "_____ motion," also called a pauper's oath in some states.

Collection Practices

Credit Bureaus

All information is removed that is _____ years old except
Chapter 7 bankruptcy which stays on _____ years.

Beware of credit clean-up scams. The only information which may be
legally removed from a credit report is _____ information.

Over _____ of the credit bureau reports have errors. You
should check your credit report every _____ to _____ years. Another
act passed in 1977 is the Federal Fair Credit Reporting Act which deals
with how credit bureaus, creditors and consumers interact.

An updated version of the Act requires a credit bureau to remove all
_____ with 30 days of notification of such inaccuracies.

To clean your credit report of inaccurate information, you should write a separate letter for each inaccuracy, staple a copy of your credit report to each letter, and circle the account number.

Note: You should request that "inquiries" be removed also. All of these letters should be sent _____ mail return receipt requested to prove when they receive the letter. If the credit bureau does not prove the accuracy of the account within 30 days, you should request they remove the _____ account from your file.

You will have to be assertive after the 30 day period.

> *"Victory belongs to the most persevering."*
>
> *Napoleon*

The Federal Trade Commission and the State Consumer Affairs division are where _____ should be lodged.

> *"Annual income twenty pounds, annual expenditure nineteen six, result happiness. Annual income twenty pounds, annual expenditure twenty pounds ought and six, result misery."*
>
> *Charles Dickens, David Copperfield*

Collection Practices

Credit Card History

CARD NAME	NUMBER	ADDRESS	PHONE #	DATE CLOSED	WRITTEN CONFIRMATION REQUESTED	WRITTEN CONFIRMATION RECIEVED
Mastercard	5555 5555 5555 5555	111 Credit Blvd., New York, NY	(201) 758-2222	8/14/2006	7/14/2006	8/28/2006

collection practices

Facts You Should Know

- Payment history on your credit file is supplied by credit grantors with whom you have credit. This includes both open accounts and accounts that have already been closed.

- Payment in full does not remove your payment history. The length of time information remains in file is:

  Credit & collection accounts-   7 years, plus 180 days, from the date of the original delinquency*

  Courthouse records-   7 years from the date filed, except bankruptcy Chapters 7 and 11 which remain for 10 years from date filed.

  *Note that creditors will attempt to extend the 7 years by re-reporting the delinquency. However, this violates the Fair Credit Reporting Act and can be challenged as an inaccuracy.

- New York state residents only: Satisfied judgments five years from the date filed; paid collections five years from the date of last activity with original creditor.

- A divorce decree does not supersede the original contract with the creditor and does not release you from legal responsibility on any accounts. You must contact each creditor individually and seek their legal binding release of your obligation. Only after that release can your credit history be updated accordingly.

- There may be what appear to be duplicate accounts reported in your credit file. This could be because some credit grantors issue both revolving and installment accounts. Another reason is that when you move, some credit grantors transfer your account to a different location and issue another account number.

- The balance reported is the balance on the date the source reported the information. Credit grantors supply information on a periodic basis, so the balance shown may not be the balance you know it is today. If the balance reported was correct as of the date reported, it is not necessary to reinvestigate the balance on that account.

- Many companies market consumer products and services by mail. If you prefer not to receive direct marketing mailings, you can write to: Mail Preference Service, Direct Marketing Association, P.O. Box 643, Carmel, New York 10512. Include your complete name, full address, and signature. They will have your name removed from these lists. This will stop most solicitations. Your name will remain on the list for five years.

- You can call the National Do Not Call Registry toll-free from the number you wish to register: 1-888-382-1222 (TTY 1-866-290-4236). This will stop most calls. You can also register online: www.ftc.gov/bcp/conline/edcams/donotcall/index.html.

- Other useful sites: www.dmaconsumers.org/cgi/offtelephone
                           www.dmaconsumers.org/cgi/offmailinglist

Credit Bureaus

The FACT Act amendments to the Fair Credit Reporting Act requires the nationwide credit bureaus to provide consumers, upon request, one free personal credit report in a 12 month period. You may contact the Central Source online at www.annualcreditreport.com or by calling toll free (877) FACT ACT. Free copies are also available if you have been denied credit in the past 60 days and the creditor used their services.

- EXPERIAN (888) 397-3742
  PO Box 2002, Allen, TX 75013
  Additional copies are $7 each. Their website is www.experian.com

- EQUIFAX CREDIT BUREAU (800) 685-1111
  PO Box 740241, Atlanta, GA 30374-0241
  Additional copies of your personal credit file are available for a small fee (up to $8) depending on your state of residence. Their website is www.equifax.com

- TRANSUNION CREDIT BUREAU (800) 888-4213
  PO Box 2000, Chester, PA 19022
  Additional copies of your personal credit file are available for $15 each depending on your state of residence. Their website is www.transunion.com

---

BE PROACTIVE

Decrease unauthorized direct mail marketing (including pre-approved credit card offers) and unwanted telemarketing calls!

How? Call the Credit Reporting Industry's Pre-Screening Opt-Out number: 1-888-567-8688 and follow the instrucitons. You can choose to be removed for 5 years or permanently. You can also add your name back if you've already opted out. They also have a website: OptOutPrescreen.com.

AND: You can write a letter and request to be removed from direct marketing databases for five years. Be sure to include your name, home phone number, address, and your signature. If your address changes, you must make another request.

For Direct Mailings:	For Telemarketing:
Mail Preference Service	Telephone Preference Service
Direct Marketing Association	Direct Marketing Association
PO Box 643, Carmel, NY 15012	PO Box 1559, Carmel, NY 15012

FEDERAL TRADE COMMISSION (202) 452-3245
6th and Pennsylvania Avenue, N.W., Washington, D.C. 20580
Publishes a brief, semi-annual list (March and September) on card pricing by the largest issuers for $5 per copy. Offers a number of free credit related publications.

Sample Removal Letter

Date _____

(From)

_____

_____

_____

VIA: Certified Mail, Return Receipt Requested
(To)
Mail Preference Service
Direct Marketing Association
P.O. Box 643
Carmel, NY 10512

RE: Unauthorized direct marketing and pre-approved credit card offers

This letter is your formal notice to remove my name from all direct marketing and pre-screening databases. I do not wish to receive any unsolicited offers, especially from credit card companies.

Not only do I request my name to be permanently removed, but I also request that my phone number and address must likewise be permanently removed. My correct information is as follows:

_____
(Complete Name)
(Full Address)
_____

_____
(Phone Number with Area Code)

Thank you for your immediate attention to this matter.

Sincerely,

(Signatures)

Collection Practices

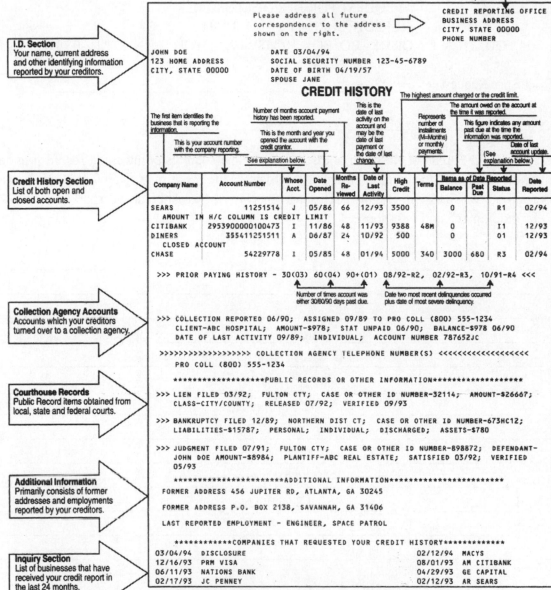

How to Read Your Credit Report

SAMPLE

The Name and Address of the office you should contact if you have any questions or disagreement with your credit report

Please address all future correspondence to the address shown on the right.

CREDIT REPORTING OFFICE
BUSINESS ADDRESS
CITY, STATE 00000
PHONE NUMBER

I.D. Section
Your name, current address and other identifying information reported by your creditors.

JOHN DOE
123 HOME ADDRESS
CITY, STATE 00000

DATE 03/04/94
SOCIAL SECURITY NUMBER 123-45-6789
DATE OF BIRTH 04/19/57
SPOUSE JANE

CREDIT HISTORY

The first item identifies the business that is reporting the information.

This is your account number with the company reporting.

Number of months account payment history has been reported.

This is the month and year you opened the account with the credit grantor. See explanation below.

This is the date of last activity on the account and may be the date of last payment or the date of last change.

The highest amount charged or the credit limit.

Represents number of installments (M=Months) or monthly payments.

The amount owed on the account at the time it was reported.

This figure indicates any amount past due at the time the information was reported. (See explanation below.)

Date of last account update.

Credit History Section
List of both open and closed accounts.

Company Name	Account Number	Whose Acct.	Date Opened	Months Re-viewed	Date of Last Activity	High Credit	Terms	Balance	Past Due	Status	Date Reported
SEARS	11251514	J	05/86	66	12/93	3500		0		R1	02/94
AMOUNT IN H/C COLUMN IS CREDIT LIMIT											
CITIBANK	2953900000100473	I	11/86	48	11/93	9388	48M	0		I1	12/93
DINERS	355411251511	A	06/87	24	10/92	500		0		01	12/93
CLOSED ACCOUNT											
CHASE	54229778	I	05/85	48	01/94	5000	340	3000	680	R3	02/94

>>> PRIOR PAYING HISTORY - 30(03) 60(04) 90+(01) 08/92-R2, 02/92-R3, 10/91-R4 <<<

Number of times account was either 30/60/90 days past due.

Date two most recent delinquencies occurred plus date of most severe delinquency.

Collection Agency Accounts
Accounts which your creditors turned over to a collection agency.

>>> COLLECTION REPORTED 06/90; ASSIGNED 09/89 TO PRO COLL (800) 555-1234
CLIENT-ABC HOSPITAL; AMOUNT-$978; STAT UNPAID 06/90; BALANCE-$978 06/90
DATE OF LAST ACTIVITY 09/89; INDIVIDUAL; ACCOUNT NUMBER 787652JC

>>>>>>>>>>>>>>>>>>>>> COLLECTION AGENCY TELEPHONE NUMBER(S) <<<<<<<<<<<<<<<<<<<<<
PRO COLL (800) 555-1234

********************PUBLIC RECORDS OR OTHER INFORMATION********************

Courthouse Records
Public Record items obtained from local, state and federal courts.

>>> LIEN FILED 03/92; FULTON CTY; CASE OR OTHER ID NUMBER-32114; AMOUNT-$26667;
CLASS-CITY/COUNTY; RELEASED 07/92; VERIFIED 09/93

>>> BANKRUPTCY FILED 12/89; NORTHERN DIST CT; CASE OR OTHER ID NUMBER-673HC12;
LIABILITIES-$15787; PERSONAL; INDIVIDUAL; DISCHARGED; ASSETS-$780

>>> JUDGMENT FILED 07/91; FULTON CTY; CASE OR OTHER ID NUMBER-898872; DEFENDANT-
JOHN DOE AMOUNT-$8984; PLANTIFF-ABC REAL ESTATE; SATISFIED 03/92; VERIFIED
05/93

Additional Information
Primarily consists of former addresses and employments reported by your creditors.

********************ADDITIONAL INFORMATION********************
FORMER ADDRESS 456 JUPITER RD, ATLANTA, GA 30245

FORMER ADDRESS P.O. BOX 2138, SAVANNAH, GA 31406

LAST REPORTED EMPLOYMENT - ENGINEER, SPACE PATROL

************COMPANIES THAT REQUESTED YOUR CREDIT HISTORY************

Inquiry Section
List of businesses that have received your credit report in the last 24 months.

03/04/94	DISCLOSURE	02/12/94	MACYS
12/16/93	PRM VISA	08/01/93	AM CITIBANK
06/11/93	NATIONS BANK	04/29/93	GE CAPITAL
02/17/93	JC PENNEY	02/12/93	AR SEARS

WHOSE ACCOUNT

Indicates who is responsible for the account and the type of participation you have with the account.

J = Joint
I = Individual
U = Undesignated
A = Authorized user
T = Terminated
M = Maker
C = Co-Maker/Co-Signer
B = On behalf of another person
S = Shared

THE FOLLOWING INQUIRIES ARE **NOT** REPORTED TO BUSINESSES:

PRM - This type of inquiry means that only your name and address were given to a credit grantor so they could offer you an application for credit. (PRM inquiries remain for six months.)

AM or AR - These inquiries indicate a periodic review of your credit history by one of your creditors. (AM and AR inquiries remain for six months.)

DISCLOSURE, ACIS or UPDATE - These inquiries indicate our activity in reponse to your contact with us for either a copy of your credit report or a request for research.

PRM, AM, AR, DISCLOSURE, ACIS and UPDATE inquiries do not show on credit reports that businesses receive, only on copies provided to you.

STATUS

Type of Account

O = Open (entire balance due each month)

R = Revolving (payment amount variable)

I = Installment (fixed number of payments)

Timeliness of Payment

0 = Approved not used; too new to rate
1 = Paid as agreed
2 = 30+ days past due
3 = 60+ days past due
4 = 90+ days past due
5 = Pays or paid 120+ days past the due date; or collection account

7 = Making regular payments under wage earner plan or similar arrangement
8 = Repossession
9 = Charged off to bad debt

Form 102249R—6-95 USA

collection practices

Request for File Disclosure Form

REQUEST FOR FILE DISCLOSURE
CREDIT BUREAU OF NASHVILLE
604 FOURTH AVE NORTH - P.O. BOX 190589 - NASHVILLE, TN 37219-0589

Reason for File Disclosure Request _____

Referred by _____ Was credit refused? yes   no

I hereby request the Credit Bureau of Nashville to disclose to me the contents of my credit record. I understand that if I have been rejected for credit within the past sixty (60) days as the result of credit information contained in my credit record, there will be NO CHARGE for this disclosure, otherwise there will be an $8 charge for an individual disclosure or $10 for both myself and my spouse.

Name _____ Phone No. _____

Spouse's Name _____

Present Address _____

City _____, State _____ Zip Code _____

Former Address _____

City _____, State _____ Zip Code _____

Date of Birth _____ Social Security No. _____

Employed By _____

How Long? _____ Position _____

Former Employment _____

Spouse's Date of Birth _____ Social Security No. _____

Spouse's Employment _____

How Long? _____ Position _____

I hereby authorize the Credit Bureau of Nashville to review my credit record with me, to make any necessary investigation of my credit transactions and to furnish to its subscribers reports based thereon. In consideration of its undertaking to make such an investigation I authorize any business or organization to give full information and records about me.

I am the person named above and I understand that Federal Law provides that a person who obtains information from a consumer reporting agency under false pretenses shall be fined not more than $5,000 or imprisoned no more than 1 year or both.

Signed _____ Date _____

Telephone Number _____ Ext _____ where I can be reached during normal working hours.

AUTHORIZATION FOR DISCLOSURE OF SPOUSE'S CREDIT RECORD

I, _____, certify that I am presently married to _____, and am acting in his/her behalf in reviewing the credit record information concerning him/her maintained by the Credit Bureau of Nashville.

collection practices

Sample Cease and Desist Letter

Date _____

(From)

_____

_____

_____

VIA: Certified Mail, Return Receipt Requested
(To)

_____

_____

_____

RE: _____

Dear _____,
This letter will serve as your legal notice under federal law that regulates the activities of collection agencies and their legal representatives.

You are hereby notified under provisions of Public Law 95-109, Section 805-C, the FAIR DEBT COLLECTION PRACTICES ACT to hereby CEASE AND DESIST in any and all attempts to collect the above debt.

Your failure to do so WILL result in charges being filed against you with the state and federal regulatory agencies empowered with enforcement.

Please be further warned that if ANY derogatory information is placed on any credit reports after receipt of this notice, it too will result in action being taken against you.

PLEASE GIVE THIS MATTER THE ATTENTION IT DESERVES.

Sincerely,

_____

(Signature)

Sample Credit Bureau Letter

Date _____

(From)

_____

_____

_____

(To)

_____ Credit Bureau

_____

_____

RE: _____

In reviewing the attached credit bureau report issued by your agency, I have detected an error regarding the following account(s) in that it is reported inaccurately.

Company Name: _____
Account Number: _____

Under the provision set forth in the 1977 Federal Fair Credit Reporting Act, I hereby request your agency to prove to me in writing the accuracy of the reporting of this account. Under the terms of the Act and succeeding court cases, you have 30 days to prove such accuracy or remove the account entirely from my report. I ask that you do so.

You will note that this letter was sent certified mail, and I expect a response within the said 30-day period. Should I not hear promptly from you, I will follow up with whatever action necessary to cause my report to be corrected.

Please feel free to call me if you have any questions. My home phone number is _____, and my office number is _____.

Sincerely,

_____
(Signature)

Collection Practices

Sample Creditor Letter

Date _____

(From)

_____

_____

_____

(To)

_____

_____

_____

RE: _____

Dear _____,

I am writing to formally request that your firm (or any agency hired by your firm) no longer contact me at my place of employment, _____.

My employer requests that calls such as yours must cease, and under the terms of the 1977 Federal Fair Debt Collection Practices Act, I formally demand all such calls to my place of employment cease. You will please take note that this letter was mailed certified mail, so I have proof that you are in receipt of this letter should legal action against you become necessary on this matter.

I am willing to pay the debt I owe you, and I will be in touch soon to work out arrangements.

Feel free to contact me at my home between _____ a.m. and _____ p.m. at the following number _____ or by mail at my home address: _____ _____.

Please give this matter the attention it deserves.

Sincerely,

_____

(Signature)

1.   For those of you who have been contacted by a creditor or collector, what emotions have you experienced?

2.   What is the best way for a creditor or collector to get paid?

3.   What are some collector stories you would like to share with us?

Answer Key (left to right)

Plan	Your	Sales
People	Telemarketers	Turnover
Emotion	You	8 a.m.
9 p.m.	Work	Except
Horrible	Bank	Wages
Paper	Pro	Rata
$10,000.00	10	Several
Slow Pay	7	10
Inaccurate	50%	1
2	Inaccuracies	Certified
Entire	Complaints	

Collection Practices

Accountability Check-Up

Collections Practices & Credit Bureaus

I. Next week is Graduation Night:
   A. Do something fun and special. For example, have a potluck with snacks, drinks and finger oods right after the video session, during the ACCOUNTABILITY and Graduation Session.
   B. Those who have attended 12 out of the 13 sessions will receive a graduation certificate.
   C. Invite a friend to visit the next session with you.

II. Be prepared to show your final budget next week! Complete column 4 of your Fiancial Snapshot.

III. Has everyone done a mission statement? Show these; share if you choose.

IV. Pull out your Testimonial Survey form from the back of the workbook. Complete and hand it in this week or next.

V. ACCOUNTABILITY & APPLICATION REVIEW: (Share your emotions with this class.)
   A. Why is it important to respond to the following statements: Run your household and do not let creditors set priorities? The best way that they can get paid is for you to take control of your financial destiny.
   B. Why is it important to respond to the following statement: I will protect my credit rating if possible; however, I will not let my creditors use it to control my life or budget.
   C. (True or False) During this program I have learned how to manage my money better so that I am not filled with stress.
   D. (True or False) I have allocated all of this month's income on paper <u>before</u> the month began. How does this help you pay off creditors?
   E. If you are in a financial mess, do you understand you did not get into financial stress quickly and you will likely walk out of it slowly?
   F. Why should you check your credit report within the next two weeks? Do you have more financial confidence now than when you started Financial Peace?
   G. Share a story with the group of your own personal experience of dealing with creditors at some point in your life.
   H. Why is it important to always pay your necessities first before paying your creditors, such as credit card companies?
   I. List some things that are necessities that must be budgeted before paying off debt.
   J. Is it wise to sign notes for family or friends? What can happen? Give an example of a true story if you have one.
   K. Talk about this thought: I will no longer allow guilt and emotion to control my financial decisions. Do you have an example of what happened when you did respond emotionally?

• •

* Be sure to complete your financial snapshot and homework the easy way online, and get great financial tools and resources for this week's lesson.

* Log in using your class code on page 22.

Footprints in the Sand

One night a man had a dream.
He dreamed he was walking
along the beach with the Lord.
Across the sky flashed scenes from his life.
He noticed two sets of footprints in the sand.
When the last scene of his life flashed before him,
he looked back at the footprints in the sand.
He noticed that many times along the
path there was only one set of footprints.

He recalled that it happened
at the very lowest and saddest
times in his life. He questioned,
"Lord, you said that once I decided to follow
you, you would walk with me all the way. Then why
during the most troublesome times in my life,
the times when I needed you most, would you
leave me?" The Lord replied, "My precious,
precious child, I love you and would never,
never leave you. During your times of trials
and suffering, when you see only
one set of footprints, it was
then that I carried you."

Collection Practices

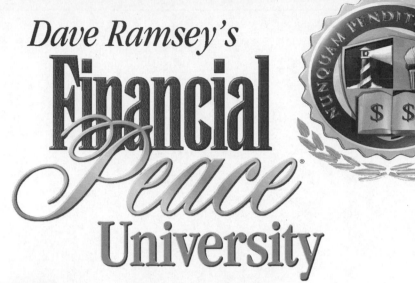

Dave Ramsey's

Financial Peace University

The Great Misunderstanding

"The earth is the Lord's and the fullness thereof..."
Psalms 24:1 (KJV)

Notes:

① Intelectual BEING → READ

② Physical BEING → Exercise

③ Emotional BEING →

④ Spiritual BEING

Serving Giving

The Great Misunderstanding

(vertical side text) great misunderstanding

236

The Great Misunderstanding

You can do everything we teach and you will prosper, but if you don't understand this lesson, you will never have Financial _____.

The Great Misunderstanding, the paradox, is that we believe that the way to have _____ is to hold on tightly.

> *"You can't shake hands with a clenched fist."*
>
> *Golda Mier*

> *"There are men who gain from their wealth only the fear of losing it."*
>
> *Antoine Riveroli*

You and I are asset _____ for the _____, so if we view it properly, we aren't giving our money anyway.

> *"The earth is the Lord's and the fullness thereof..."*
>
> *Psalms 24:1 (KJV)*

A _Steward_ is a manager not an _Owner_.

Andrew Carnegie, wealthy steel magnate from 1900, said, "Surplus wealth is a sacred trust to be managed for the good of others."

Why does God tell us to _Give_ so often?

Giving makes us _More_ Christ-like; a spiritually mature Christian gives.

Giving _Mores_ you to become less _Selfish_, and less selfish people have more of a tendency to prosper in relationships and in wealth.

Because we are designed in God's image, we are happiest and most fulfilled when _Serving_ and _Giving_.

The Great Misunderstanding

The Great Misunderstanding

Provide and Protect

Giving is:

1) a _Reminder_ of _Ownership_

> *"The earth is the Lord's and the fullness thereof..."*
>
> *Psalms 24:1 (KJV)*

2) _PRAISE_ and _WORSHIP_

> *"...for God loves a cheerful giver."*
>
> *II Corinthians 9:7 (KJV)*

3) _SPIRITUAL_ _Warfare_

> *"'And I will rebuke the devourer for your sakes, So that he will not destroy the fruit of your ground, Nor shall the vine fail to bear fruit for you in the field,' says the Lord of Hosts."*
>
> *Malachi 3:11 (NKJV)*

> *"...together with a freewill offering for the house of God..."*
>
> *Ezra 1:4 (NASV)*

Instructions for Giving

The tithe is a tenth (10%) of your ___Increase___.

> *"When you have finished paying all the tithe of your increase..."*
> *Deuteronomy 26:12 (NASV)*

"Give first fruits" means off the ___Top___.

The tithe is to go to your ___Local Church___ which provides the same function as the Old Testament ___Store house___.

Offerings are different than the tithe. Offerings are ___Above___ the tithe and are from surplus. They are ___Free Will___.

The tithe is ___Pre Law___.

> *"And this stone, which I have set up as a pillar, will be God's house; and of that Thou dost give me I will surely give a tenth to Thee."*
> *Genesis 28:22 (NASV)*

The tithe is New ___Testament___.

> *"Woe to you, scribes and Pharisees, hypocrites! For you pay tithe of mint and anise and cummin, and have neglected the weightier matters of the law: justice and mercy and faith. These you ought to have done, without leaving the others undone."*
> *Matthew 23:23 and Luke 11:42*

Never give with the ___Motive___ of having your giving returned.

Financial Peace is more than just God's system for understanding money, becoming debt free, and building wealth.

Financial Peace is when the Great Misunderstanding becomes ___understood___.

The Great Misunderstanding

When this happens not only will your whole outlook change, but then you will begin to impact those you love. When you give these concepts away, you will have reached a full _understanding_ of Financial Peace.

> *"And if I give all my possessions to the poor, and if I deliver my body to be burned, but do not have love, it profits me nothing."*
>
> **I Corinthians 13:3 (NASV)**

> *"The Pharisee stood and prayed thus with himself... I give tithes of all that I possess."*
>
> **Luke 18:11 & 12 (NKJV)**

> *"And all the tithe of the land, whether of the seed of the land or of the fruit of the tree, is the Lord's. It is holy to the Lord."*
>
> **Leviticus 27:30 (NKJV)**

> *"You shall surely tithe all of the produce from what you sow, which come out of the field every year."*
>
> **Deuteronomy 14:22 (NASV)**

> *"Bring all the tithes into the storehouse, that there may be food in My house..."*
>
> **Malachi 3:10 (NKJV)**

> *"...bring up the tenth of the tithes to the house of our God, to the chambers of the storehouse."*
>
> **Nehemiah 10:2 (NASV)**

Discussion Questions

1. Why does the Lord ask us to give?

2. What are some of the reasons we don't give?

3. How do you feel when you give? When you don't?

4. What does that tell you about giving?

5. Relate some stories of God's provision in your life.

Answer Key (left to right)

Peace	More	Managers
Lord	Steward	Owner
Give	More	Moves
Selfish	Serving	Giving
Reminder	Ownership	Praise
Worship	Spiritual	Warfare
Increase	Top	Local
Church	Storehouse	Above
Free-will	Pre-law	Testament
Motive	Understood	Understanding

The Great Misunderstanding

Accountability Check-Up

The Great Misunderstanding

I.   Enjoy finger foods, drinks and potluck items during the video lesson. After the video lesson, form a discussion circle.

II. Show your final zero-based budget. Congratulations!
    A. Hand in your completed Financial Snapshot (back copy).
    B. Share victory stories with class about how the program helped you.

III. Add up grand total of class debt paid off and credit card debt avoided.
    A. Count up how many credit cards were cut up over 13 weeks.
    B. Add up how much, as a group, was put into emergency funds and savings. Do this by passing out 3 x 5 cards with no names on them and have everyone list the above information.

IV. The class coordinator will hand out graduation certificates.

V.   Everyone is invited to consider helping bring FPU to your community, church, school, or business, etc. by becoming a class coordinator.

VI. Hand in your Testimonial Survey forms tonight to your coordinator.
    A. Let the coordinator know how much you appreciate him/her for volunteering to host this class.
    B. Share with the coordinator something he/she did that helped you over the past 13 weeks.

VII. Final ACCOUNTABILITY & APPLICATION REVIEW:
    A. How would it feel to be able to start giving away money?
    B. Have the spiritual principles of this program helped you seek God and His will for your life? If so, how?
    C. Why is it important to give to your church while paying off debts?
    D. How has your personal spiritual growth helped you apply the principles of this program?
    E. How does viewing yourself as a manager of God's resources affect your thnking and behavior about money?
    F. Do you honestly believe other people need to learn about this program and how it can help change their lives? If so, what will you do about it?
    G. How will you be handling God's money and family relationships differently than you did before starting this 13-week program?

VIII. SPECIAL NOTE TO CLASS LEADER: Return final class attendance roster, student's Financial Snapshots, Testimonial Surveys, class totals of debt paid off and amount saved, and names of potential coordinators to the FPU office.

Financial Peace University
1749 Mallory Lane, Suite 100
Brentwood, TN 37027

great misunderstanding

* Be sure to complete your homework the easy way online, and get great financial tools and resources for this week's lesson.
* Log in using your class code on page 22.

The **Share It!** program is dedicated to helping organizations spread financial literacy throughout their communities. Your gift, along with many others, helps individuals, families, and students to become financially self-sufficient by combining accountability with education. **Share It!** provides financial literacy material for those being helped by:

- Housing Initiatives
- Welfare-to-work projects
- Domestic violence shelters
- Drug and alcohol recovery programs
- Crisis pregnancy centers
- Youth outreach and high school curriculum

Make donations online at:

www.shareittoday.org

Or mail your donation to:

Share It!
Financial Peace University, Inc.
Charitable Contributions
1749 Mallory Lane, Suite 200
Brentwood, TN 37027

See the Share It! link at **www.daveramsey.com** for updates and exclusive content online!

Please tear the following pages on their perforated edges.

Attention All FPU Members!

We need your help to change the direction of this nation.

We invite you to become a part of our team by becoming a volunteer coordinator. For more information on how you can help, call Dave Ramsey's office at 1-888-227-3223 and ask how you can become part of Dave's FPU Coordinator TEAM or check it out on the web at www.daveramsey.com.

Complete the FPU Coordinator Application on the reverse side and send it into our office immediately. Once we receive your application, we will send you all the information you need to get started.

40149

Coordinator Application

toll free: (888) 227-3223   local: (615) 371-8881
fax: (615) 620-6398   www.daveramsey.com

Dave Ramsey's
Financial Peace University

PERSONAL INFORMATION

The Lampo Group, Inc. is not a multi-level, insurance or investment based company. Are you currently involved in any of those three fields of work?   ○ Yes   ○ No

FIRST NAME

LAST NAME

MAILING ADDRESS

CITY

STATE   ZIP CODE   ( ) -   DAYTIME PHONE NUMBER

EMAIL ADDRESS

Please provide type of organization and organizational information you would like to coordinate for

○ Church
○ Workplace
○ Literacy Program/Nonprofit Org
○ Military
○ Hispanic Group
○ Community/University/College

ORGANIZATION NAME

CITY   STATE   ORG SIZE

○ Church
○ Workplace
○ Literacy Program/Nonprofit Org
○ Military
○ Hispanic Group
○ Community/University/College

ORGANIZATION NAME

CITY   STATE   ORG SIZE

Please select your level of interest: ○ I am gathering information now.
                                          ○ I plan on starting Financial Peace University.
                                          ○ I plan to start Financial Peace University in the next month.

Other areas of interest:
○ I am interested in becoming one of **Dave's Certified Counselors.**   ○ For Profit   ○ Ministry
○ I am interested in a curriculum for youth groups and high school students.

SCHOOL/CHURCH NAME

CITY   STATE ZIP CODE

40149

1/10/06

Educational Materials

Financial Peace University

FPU DVD Series...$150.00
  All 13 FPU video lessons *(available to FPU members only)*.

FPU Compact Disc Library..$29.95
  All 13 FPU audio lessons in CD format *(available only to FPU members at this price)*.

Deluxe Executive FPU Envelope System.......................................$19.95
  Includes 10 envelopes, recording sheets, instructions, plus checkbook pocket, debit card slots, note pad and coin/coupon pouch.

Women's Designer FPU Envelope System.......................................$19.95
  Includes 10 envelopes, recording sheets, instructions, checkbook pocket (except pink/orange), debit card slots, and zippered coin pocket. Available in red, brown/blue, or pink/orange.

FPU Starter Envelope System..$9.95
  Includes 10 envelopes and recording sheets.

FPU Envelope System Refills...$4.95
  Includes 10 envelopes and recording sheets.

FPU Memo Pad...$1.95

New FPU Bonus Pak CD..$4.95
  Includes Orientation Video; Reality Check; web links; all printable financial forms; several financial calculators; and much more!

FPU Debit Card Holder (Qty. 2)..$1.95
  Warning: "Using this card may be hazardous to your financial health." CONTROLS your use of ATM and debit cards and reminds you NOT to use those cards impulsively.

Financial Peace University Home Study Course.............................. $289.00
  Includes 13 video lessons on DVD, FPU workbook with budgeting forms, *Financial Peace Revisited* book, envelope system and all 13 FPU lessons on audio CDs. (FOR HOME USE ONLY!)

Replacement FPU Workbook..$14.95
  All 13 FPU lessons *(available to FPU members only)*.

To place an order, please complete the Educational Materials Order Form on the reverse side and mail it to the Lampo Office. Prices subject to change without notice.
To verify current price, check our website at daveramsey.com or call Customer Care at 888-227-3223.

247

Dave Ramsey's Financial Peace University

The Lampo Group, Inc.
1749 Mallory Lane, Suite 100
Brentwood, TN 37027

Your Coach to a TOTAL MONEY MAKEOVER!

EDUCATIONAL MATERIALS ORDER FORM

toll free: (888) 227-3223
local: (615) 371-8881
fax: (615) 620-6398
web: www.daveramsey.com

FIRST NAME

LAST NAME

ADDRESS

CITY   STATE   ZIP CODE   ( )   PRIMARY PHONE

EMAIL ADDRESS

QTY	FPU ITEMS	UNIT PRICE	TOTAL AMOUNT
	FPU Starter Envelope System	$9.95	.
	FPU Deluxe Envelope System	$19.95	.
	FPU Envelope System Refills	$4.95	.
	FPU Compact Disc Library (Members only)	$29.95	.
	FPU DVD Library (Members only)	$150.00	.
			.
		Subtotal	.
		Sales Tax (TN residents add 9.25%)	.
		Shipping and handling (add 12% - $5.00 minimum)	.

Payment Information

I AM PAYING THIS TOTAL AMOUNT: $ _____ . __

I AM PAYING WITH:

○ Cash   ○ Check # _____ payable to The Lampo Group, Inc.   ○ Debit Card (enter info below)

For Debit Card:

THE NAME ON MY DEBIT CARD IS:

FIRST NAME   M.I.   LAST NAME

DEBIT CARD NO.   EXPIRATION DATE (MM/YY) __ / __

SIGN HERE X _____

ALLOW 2 WEEKS FOR DELIVERY
Check out www.daveramsey.com for more products

32405

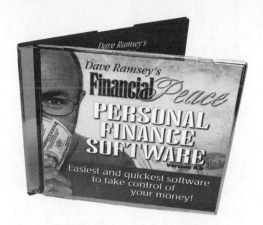
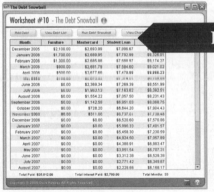

249

TESTIMONIAL SURVEY

CLASS LOCATION CODE
⬜⬜⬜⬜⬜⬜

CLASS START DATE (MM/DD/YY)
⬜⬜ / ⬜⬜ / ⬜⬜

COORDINATOR FIRST NAME
⬜⬜⬜⬜⬜⬜⬜⬜⬜⬜⬜⬜

COORDINATOR LAST NAME
⬜⬜⬜⬜⬜⬜⬜⬜⬜⬜⬜⬜⬜⬜⬜⬜⬜⬜⬜

How did you hear about Financial Peace University?
○ Family   ○ Website   ○ FPU Member   ○ The Dave Ramsey Show
○ Friend   ○ Live Event   ○ Television   ○ Radio Commercials
○ Newspaper   ○ Coordinator   ○ Church Bulletin   ○ Bookstore
○ Other [_____]

How would you rate your situation when you started FPU?
○ 1   ○ 2   ○ 3   ○ 4   ○ 5   ○ 6   ○ 7   ○ 8   ○ 9   ○ 10
Financially distressed   Financially secure

Overall, how well do you feel FPU has helped you improve your financial self-confidence, peace of mind and sense of security, compared to your personal financial life before attending FPU?
○ 1   ○ 2   ○ 3   ○ 4   ○ 5   ○ 6   ○ 7   ○ 8   ○ 9   ○ 10
Little improvement   Big improvement

Can you better manage your money now as a result of attending FPU?   ○ Yes   ○ No

Do you feel you would benefit from a one-on-one counseling session?   ○ Yes   ○ No

How much debt have you been able to pay off since you first learned of the Financial Peace principles? $[_____].00

How much money have you been able to save since you started applying the Financial Peace principles?
$[_____].00 Emergency fund $[_____].00 Total

Which lesson or lessons were the most beneficial and helpful to you?
[_____]

How much impact has this program had on your personal relationships?
○ 1   ○ 2   ○ 3   ○ 4   ○ 5   ○ 6   ○ 7   ○ 8   ○ 9   ○ 10
Little   Greatly

What has Financial Peace University done for you? (Please print)
[_____]

How would you rate your volunteer Coordinator?
○ 1   ○ 2   ○ 3   ○ 4   ○ 5   ○ 6   ○ 7   ○ 8   ○ 9   ○ 10
Needs Improvement   Excellent

50949

FPU Membership Information

FIRST NAME

LAST NAME

ADDRESS

CITY

STATE   ZIP CODE

PRIMARY PHONE

EMAIL ADDRESS

Are you interested in becoming involved as an FPU Coordinator or Group Leader?   ○ YES   ○ NO

Why?

Do we at The Lampo Group have your permission to use this information as a testimonial to the power of this program?   ○ YES   ○ NO

AGE   ○ <18   ○ 18-25   ○ 26-35   ○ 36-45   ○ 46-55   ○ 56-65   ○ 65+

MARITAL STATUS   ○ Single   ○ Married   ○ Divorced   ○ Widowed

RACE   ○ Caucasian   ○ African American   ○ Hispanic   ○ Asian   ○ Other

SIZE OF FAMILY   ○ 1   ○ 2   ○ 3   ○ 4   ○ 5   ○ 6+

REGULAR CHURCH ATTENDANCE   ○ YES   ○ NO

HOUSEHOLD INCOME   ○ <15,000   ○ 15,000-30,000   ○ 30,000-50,000   ○ 50,000-80,000   ○ 80,000-100,000   ○ 100,000+

COLLEGE   ○ YES   ○ NO   INTERNET USER   ○ YES   ○ NO

BUSINESS OWNER   ○ YES   ○ NO   PAST BANKRUPTCY   ○ YES   ○ NO

Recommendations for Financial Peace University

If you believe your employer, company or church would be interested in setting up the Financial Peace University program for the employees or church members, please list the person for us to contact.

CHURCH OR COMPANY NAME

CONTACT - FIRST NAME

CONTACT - LAST NAME

EMAIL ADDRESS

If you believe that the FPU program, or a one-on-one counseling session, would benefit your friends, family members, co-workers, etc., please fill in the information below so we can email them information about our program.

FIRST NAME

LAST NAME

EMAIL ADDRESS

FIRST NAME

LAST NAME

EMAIL ADDRESS

Submit this form to your coordinator or return to:
The Lampo Group, Inc.   ◆   1749 Mallory Lane, Suite 100   ◆   Brentwood, Tennessee 37027

50949

252

Monthly Cash Flow Plan

Sheet 5

Budgeted Item	Sub Total	TOTAL	Actually Spent	% of Take Home Pay
CHARITABLE GIFTS		_____	_____	_____
SAVING				
Emergency Fund	_____		_____	
Retirement Fund	_____		_____	
College Fund	_____	_____	_____	_____
HOUSING				
First Mortgage	_____		_____	
Second Mortgage	_____		_____	
Real Estate Taxes	_____		_____	
Homeowners Ins.	_____		_____	
Repairs or Mn. Fee	_____		_____	
Replace Furniture	_____		_____	
Other _____	_____	_____	_____	_____
UTILITIES				
Electricity	_____		_____	
Water	_____		_____	
Gas	_____		_____	
Phone	_____		_____	
Trash	_____		_____	
Cable	_____	_____	_____	_____
***FOOD**				
*Grocery	_____		_____	
*Restaurants	_____	_____	_____	_____
TRANSPORTATION				
Car Payment	_____		_____	
Car Payment	_____		_____	
*Gas and Oil	_____		_____	
*Repairs and Tires	_____		_____	
Car Insurance	_____		_____	
License and Taxes	_____		_____	
Car Replacement	_____	_____	_____	_____
PAGE 1 TOTAL		_____	_____	

Monthly Cash Flow Plan

Budgeted Item	Sub Total	TOTAL	Actually Spent	% of Take Home Pay
*CLOTHING				
*Children	_____		_____	
*Adults	_____		_____	
*Cleaning/Laundry	_____	_____	_____	_____
MEDICAL/HEALTH				
Disability Insurance	_____		_____	
Health Insurance	_____		_____	
Doctor Bills	_____		_____	
Dentist	_____		_____	
Optometrist	_____		_____	
Drugs	_____	_____	_____	_____
PERSONAL				
Life Insurance	_____		_____	
Child Care	_____		_____	
*Baby Sitter	_____		_____	
*Toiletries	_____		_____	
*Cosmetics	_____		_____	
*Hair Care	_____		_____	
Education/Adult	_____		_____	
School Tuition	_____		_____	
School Supplies	_____		_____	
Child Support	_____		_____	
Alimony	_____		_____	
Subscriptions	_____		_____	
Organization Dues	_____		_____	
Gifts (inc. Christmas)	_____		_____	
Miscellaneous	_____		_____	
*BLOW $$	_____	_____	_____	_____
PAGE 2 TOTAL		_____		

Monthly Cash Flow Plan

Budgeted Item	Sub Total	TOTAL	Actually Spent	% of Take Home Pay
RECREATION				
*Entertainment	_____		_____	
Vacation	_____	_____	_____	
DEBTS (Hopefully -0-)				
Visa 1	_____		_____	
Visa 2	_____		_____	
MasterCard 1	_____		_____	
MasterCard 2	_____		_____	
American Express	_____		_____	
Discover Card	_____		_____	
Gas Card 1	_____		_____	
Gas Card 2	_____		_____	
Dept. Store Card 1	_____		_____	
Dept. Store Card 2	_____		_____	
Finance Co. 1	_____		_____	
Finance Co. 2	_____		_____	
Credit Line	_____		_____	
Student Loan 1	_____		_____	
Student Loan 2	_____		_____	
Other _____	_____		_____	
Other _____	_____		_____	
Other _____	_____		_____	
Other _____	_____		_____	
Other _____	_____	_____	_____	
PAGE 3 TOTAL		_____	_____	
PAGE 2 TOTAL		_____	_____	
PAGE 1 TOTAL		_____	_____	
GRAND TOTAL		_____	_____	

TOTAL HOUSEHOLD INCOME _____

ZERO

Monthly Cash Flow Plan

Sheet 5

Budgeted Item	Sub Total	TOTAL	Actually Spent	% of Take Home Pay
CHARITABLE GIFTS		_____	_____	_____
SAVING				
Emergency Fund	_____		_____	
Retirement Fund	_____		_____	
College Fund	_____		_____	
HOUSING				
First Mortgage	_____		_____	
Second Mortgage	_____		_____	
Real Estate Taxes	_____		_____	
Homeowners Ins.	_____		_____	
Repairs or Mn. Fee	_____		_____	
Replace Furniture	_____		_____	
Other _____	_____	_____	_____	_____
UTILITIES				
Electricity	_____		_____	
Water	_____		_____	
Gas	_____		_____	
Phone	_____		_____	
Trash	_____		_____	
Cable	_____	_____	_____	_____
***FOOD**				
*Grocery	_____		_____	
*Restaurants	_____	_____	_____	_____
TRANSPORTATION				
Car Payment	_____		_____	
Car Payment	_____		_____	
*Gas and Oil	_____		_____	
*Repairs and Tires	_____		_____	
Car Insurance	_____		_____	
License and Taxes	_____		_____	
Car Replacement	_____	_____	_____	_____
PAGE 1 TOTAL		_____	_____	

Monthly Cash Flow Plan

Sheet 5 Continued

Budgeted Item	Sub Total	TOTAL	Actually Spent	% of Take Home Pay
*CLOTHING				
*Children	_____		_____	
*Adults	_____		_____	
*Cleaning/Laundry	_____	_____	_____	_____
MEDICAL/HEALTH				
Disability Insurance	_____		_____	
Health Insurance	_____		_____	
Doctor Bills	_____		_____	
Dentist	_____		_____	
Optometrist	_____		_____	
Drugs	_____	_____	_____	_____
PERSONAL				
Life Insurance	_____		_____	
Child Care	_____		_____	
*Baby Sitter	_____		_____	
*Toiletries	_____		_____	
*Cosmetics	_____		_____	
*Hair Care	_____		_____	
Education/Adult	_____		_____	
School Tuition	_____		_____	
School Supplies	_____		_____	
Child Support	_____		_____	
Alimony	_____		_____	
Subscriptions	_____		_____	
Organization Dues	_____		_____	
Gifts (inc. Christmas)	_____		_____	
Miscellaneous	_____		_____	
*BLOW $$	_____	_____	_____	_____
PAGE 2 TOTAL		_____		

Monthly Cash Flow Plan

Sheet 5 Continued

Budgeted Item	Sub Total	TOTAL	Actually Spent	% of Take Home Pay
RECREATION				
*Entertainment	_____		_____	
Vacation	_____	_____	_____	_____
DEBTS (Hopefully -0-)				
Visa 1	_____		_____	
Visa 2	_____		_____	
MasterCard 1	_____		_____	
MasterCard 2	_____		_____	
American Express	_____		_____	
Discover Card	_____		_____	
Gas Card 1	_____		_____	
Gas Card 2	_____		_____	
Dept. Store Card 1	_____		_____	
Dept. Store Card 2	_____		_____	
Finance Co. 1	_____		_____	
Finance Co. 2	_____		_____	
Credit Line	_____		_____	
Student Loan 1	_____		_____	
Student Loan 2	_____		_____	
Other _____	_____		_____	
Other _____	_____		_____	
Other _____	_____		_____	
Other _____	_____		_____	
Other _____	_____	_____	_____	_____
PAGE 3 TOTAL		_____	_____	
PAGE 2 TOTAL		_____	_____	
PAGE 1 TOTAL		_____	_____	
GRAND TOTAL		_____	_____	
TOTAL HOUSEHOLD INCOME	_____			
	ZERO			

Monthly Cash Flow Plan

Budgeted Item	Sub Total	TOTAL	Actually Spent	% of Take Home Pay
CHARITABLE GIFTS		_____	_____	_____
SAVING				
Emergency Fund	_____			
Retirement Fund	_____			
College Fund	_____	_____	_____	_____
HOUSING				
First Mortgage	_____			
Second Mortgage	_____			
Real Estate Taxes	_____			
Homeowners Ins.	_____			
Repairs or Mn. Fee	_____			
Replace Furniture	_____			
Other _____	_____	_____	_____	_____
UTILITIES				
Electricity	_____			
Water	_____			
Gas	_____			
Phone	_____			
Trash	_____			
Cable	_____	_____	_____	_____
***FOOD**				
*Grocery	_____			
*Restaurants	_____	_____	_____	_____
TRANSPORTATION				
Car Payment	_____			
Car Payment	_____			
*Gas and Oil	_____			
*Repairs and Tires	_____			
Car Insurance	_____			
License and Taxes	_____			
Car Replacement	_____	_____	_____	_____
PAGE 1 TOTAL			_____	_____

✓ Monthly Cash Flow Plan

Budgeted Item	Sub Total	TOTAL	Actually Spent	% of Take Home Pay
*CLOTHING				
*Children	_____		_____	
*Adults	_____		_____	
*Cleaning/Laundry	_____	_____	_____	_____
MEDICAL/HEALTH				
Disability Insurance	_____		_____	
Health Insurance	_____		_____	
Doctor Bills	_____		_____	
Dentist	_____		_____	
Optometrist	_____		_____	
Drugs	_____	_____	_____	_____
PERSONAL				
Life Insurance	_____		_____	
Child Care	_____		_____	
*Baby Sitter	_____		_____	
*Toiletries	_____		_____	
*Cosmetics	_____		_____	
*Hair Care	_____		_____	
Education/Adult	_____		_____	
School Tuition	_____		_____	
School Supplies	_____		_____	
Child Support	_____		_____	
Alimony	_____		_____	
Subscriptions	_____		_____	
Organization Dues	_____		_____	
Gifts (inc. Christmas)	_____		_____	
Miscellaneous	_____		_____	
*BLOW $$	_____	_____	_____	_____
PAGE 2 TOTAL		_____		

Monthly Cash Flow Plan

Sheet 5 Continued

Budgeted Item	Sub Total	TOTAL	Actually Spent	% of Take Home Pay
RECREATION				
*Entertainment	_____		_____	
Vacation	_____	_____	_____	_____
DEBTS (Hopefully -0-)				
Visa 1	_____		_____	
Visa 2	_____		_____	
MasterCard 1	_____		_____	
MasterCard 2	_____		_____	
American Express	_____		_____	
Discover Card	_____		_____	
Gas Card 1	_____		_____	
Gas Card 2	_____		_____	
Dept. Store Card 1	_____		_____	
Dept. Store Card 2	_____		_____	
Finance Co. 1	_____		_____	
Finance Co. 2	_____		_____	
Credit Line	_____		_____	
Student Loan 1	_____		_____	
Student Loan 2	_____		_____	
Other _____	_____		_____	
Other _____	_____		_____	
Other _____	_____		_____	
Other _____	_____		_____	
Other _____	_____	_____	_____	_____
PAGE 3 TOTAL		_____	_____	
PAGE 2 TOTAL		_____	_____	
PAGE 1 TOTAL		_____	_____	
GRAND TOTAL		_____	_____	
TOTAL HOUSEHOLD INCOME	_____			

ZERO

Addendum Four

MSA's vs. HSA's

	MSA	HSA
Individual	$1,700 min. Deductible 65% of deductible can be saved	$1,050 min. Deductible 100% of deductible can be saved
Families	$3,350 min. Deductible 75% of deductible can be saved	$2,100 min. Deductible 100% of deductible can be saved

The exceptions to the above information are that there is a maximum contribution on HSA's of $2,700 for indidviduals and $5,450 for families. If your deductible is more than that, you're out of luck.

* Age 55+: Extra Contributions
>   2006 .... $700
>   2007 .... $800
>   2008 .... $900
>   2009 (and after) $1,000

* Penalty for non-medical withdrawl:
    It's treated as if it were income, then slapped with an extra 10% fine.

401(k): A "qualified retirement plan" for corporations, cash or deferred arrangement.

403(b): A "qualified retirement plan" for nonprofit groups such as churches, hospitals and schools, cash or deferred arrangement.

457 plan: This is a "deferred compensation" retirement plan for state and local government employees.

529 plan: A college savings plan that allows individuals to save on a tax-deferred basis in order to fund future college and graduate school expenses of a child or beneficiary. Generally sponsored by a state, these are professionally managed investments.

12b-1 fee: An annual fee that some mutual funds charge to pay for marketing and distribution activities.

Accountability: Taking responsibility. An "accountability partner" assists people in making wise decisions about life and money.

Active: Money is very active. It is always moving and can be utilized in many ways.

Active management: Portfolio management that seeks to exceed the returns of the financial markets. Active managers rely on research, market forecast, and their own judgment and experience in making investment decisions.

Adjustable Rate Mortgage (ARM): These were brought on as a result of high interest rates in the early 1980s. Banks wanted to transfer the risk of higher interest rates to the consumer, so with these loans, you start out with a lower rate and it increases over time. You do not want to get an ARM.

Aggressive growth stock mutual fund: A mutual fund that seeks to provide maximum long-term capital growth from stocks of primarily smaller companies or narrow market segments. Dividend income is incidental. This is the most volatile fund and is invested in smaller companies. Also referred to as a small-cap fund.

Allowance: To make exception for.

Ambition: One's goal and desires in life (i.e. career goals).

Amoral: Lacking morals; neither good nor bad. Money is amoral; it can be used for good or bad.

Amortization table: A table that shows how much of each payment will be applied toward principal and how much toward interest over the life of the loan. It also shows the gradual decrease of the loan balance until it reaches zero.

Annuity: A type of investment where the money is guaranteed by an insurance company. It is a savings plan through an insurance company.

Appraisal: An opinion of value.

Appreciation: An increase in value.

Annual Percentage Rate (APR): When financing, this is used to determine the percentage of interest one pays to the lender.

Asset: Anything that is owned by an individual. With respect to saving and investing, assets are generally categorized as liquid (cash) and capital (investment) assets.

Asset allocation: The process of deciding how your investment dollars will be apportioned among various classes of financial assets, such as stocks, bonds and cash investments.

Asset allocation fund: A type of "balanced" mutual fund whose investment advisor may change the fund's mix of stocks, bonds or cash investments in an effort to find the best balance between risk and potential return.

Asset classes: Major categories of financial assets or securities. The three primary classes are common stocks, bonds and cash investments.

Assumption loan: This is when a potential homebuyer pays the seller the equity in the home and then takes over the payments.

ATM card: The Automated Teller Card allows you to make transactions at the bank's automated teller machines.

Auctions: A public sale in which property or items of merchandise are sold to the highest bidder. Auctions are great places to find deals, but be careful and do your research.

Auto insurance: Insurance to protect a car owner in the event of an accident or damage to the vehicle. Make sure you have adequate liability with auto insurance!

Average annual return: The rate of return on investments averaged over a specific period of time. It is determined by adding together the rates of return for each year and dividing it by the number of years in the calculation.

Baby steps: The seven steps to a healthy financial plan.

Back-end load: A sales commission paid when the investor sells mutual fund shares. Some funds gradually phase out back-end loads over several years. Also called redemption fee or contingent deferred sales charge.

Balanced fund: A mutual fund that invests in more than one type of financial asset: stocks, bonds, and in some cases, cash investments.

Balloon mortgage: A mortgage where, for a set period of time, the interest is lower than normal. However, the entire loan amount becomes due at the end of the term of the loan.

Bankrupt: To declare bankruptcy. See bankruptcy.

Bankruptcy: A legal procedure for dealing with debt problems of individuals and businesses. Specifically, a case filed under one of the chapters of Title 11 of the United States Code (the Bankruptcy Code).

Banks: Corporations chartered by state or federal government to offer numerous financial services such as checking and savings accounts, loans and safe deposit boxes. The Federal Deposit Insurance Corporation (FDIC) insures accounts in federally chartered banks.

Bargains: These are deals obtained when negotiating and you pay a lesser price than asked for an item.

Beneficiary: The recipient of assets passed on from the death of a friend or relative.

Bill of sale: A written document that transfers title of personal property.

Bond: A debt instrument where a company owes you money. The rate of return on these is low. A form of I.O.U. issued by corporation, government or government agencies. The issuer makes regular interest payments on the bond and promises to pay back or redeem the face value of the bond, at a specified point in the future (the maturity date). Bonds may be issued for terms of up to 30 or more years.

Bond mutual fund: Mutual funds that buy and sell bonds.

Break-even analysis: A method used to evaluate whether or not it is fiscally responsible to make changes or additions in one's insurance deductible(s).

Budget: A cash flow plan. A budget gives every dollar a name at the beginning of the month.

Buyer's remorse: Regretting a purchase soon after making it.

Capital gain: A positive difference between an asset's price when bought and its price when or if sold; the opposite of capital loss.

Capital gain distribution: Payment to mutual fund shareholders of any gains realized during the year on securities that have been sold at a profit. Capital gains are distributed on a net basis, after subtracting any capital losses for the year. When losses exceed gains for the year, the difference may be carried forward and subtracted from future gains.

Capital loss: A negative difference between an asset's price when bought and its price when or if sold; the opposite of capital gain.

Career: This is your line of work.

Cash investments: Investments in interest-bearing bank deposits, money market instruments and U.S. Treasury bills or notes. These contain maturities ranging in income and capital gains of an investment.

Cash value insurance: Life insurance that is expensive in order to fund a savings plan with it.

Catastrophic: To have a major, negative financial event (i.e., to lose your home due to fire).

CD: Certificate of Deposit, usually at a bank. This is just a savings account with a little higher interest rate because you are agreeing to tie up your money for a little while (six months, one year, etc.).

Chapter 7 bankruptcy: The chapter of the Bankruptcy Code providing for liquidation (i.e. the sale of a debtor's nonexempt property and the distribution of the proceeds to creditors).

Chapter 11 bankruptcy: A reorganization bankruptcy, usually involving a corporation or partnership. A Chapter 11 debtor usually proposes a plan of reorganization to keep a business alive and pay creditors over time.

Chapter 13 bankruptcy: The chapter of the Bankruptcy Code providing for adjustment of debts of an individual with regular income. Chapter 13 allows a debtor to keep property and pay debts over time, usually three to five years.

Check card: A type of card issued by a bank and used to make purchases. The money comes directly out of your checking account.

Checking account: Account set up to maintain your daily financial activities. Users can draft checks for payment, issue deposits into their accounts and keep track of their debit card transactions through their checking account.

Claim: Paperwork filed with an insurance company in order to get them to cover a loss.

Co-insurance: In a health insurance policy, after you pay the deductible, the insurance company pays a percentage and you pay a percentage; 80/20 - insurance pays 80 percent and you pay 20 percent.

College fund: Money set aside in investments that will grow for college expenses.

Collision: The portion of auto insurance that covers losses due to auto damage in an accident.

Commission: This is what you should pay children instead of allowances; they do chores to earn money, as opposed to just handing them money without them working for it.

Commodities: A commodity is food, metal or other fixed physical substance that investors buy or sell, usually via futures contracts.

Compensation: The total wages or salary and benefits that an employee receives. Also called income.

Compound interest: Interest paid on interest earned. Interest is credited daily, monthly, quarterly, semi-annually or annually on both principal and previously credited interest.

Comprehensive: Pays for damage to your car that is not the result of an accident.

Consignment shop: Retail facility where people can sell their items and the owner of the facility retains a percentage of the sale.

Consumer: A person who buys and/or uses a product.

Contact letter: A letter informing a prospective employer that you are interested in working for their organization. Usually accompanied with or followed by a resume.

Contents policy: An insurance policy that covers your possessions in a home or apartment.

Conventional loan: These are loans obtained through the Federal National Mortgage Association (FNMA), which insures them against default; down payments range from 5 to 20 percent or more.

Co-pay: In regards to health insurance, it is paying a set amount per visit. Co-pay expenses will vary depending upon the policy.

Co-signing: Signing a note to guarantee someone else's loan. If they default on the loan, you have to pay.

Cottage industries: In-home businesses.

Couponing: When you use coupons to save money on groceries or other items.

Cover letter: Similar to the contact letter, the cover letter is used to inform the prospective employer of your interest and capabilities as they relate to the employment opportunity.

Coverage: Applies to the amount of protection you have through an insurance company in the event of a loss.

Credit: Money loaned.

Credit bureau: An agency that collects the credit history of consumers so that creditors can make decisions about granting loans.

Credit card: Tool used to finance a purchase.

Credit disability: Insurance that pays for financed items or purchases if you become disabled and are unable to earn an income.

Credit laws:

Fair Credit Reporting Act (1971): Federal law that covers the reporting of debt repayment information. It establishes when a credit reporting agency may provide a report to someone; states that obsolete information must be taken off (seven to 10 years); gives consumers the right to know what is in their credit report; requires that both a credit bureau and information provider (i.e. department store) have an obligation to correct wrong information; gives consumers the right to dispute inaccurate information and add a 100-word statement to their report to explain accurate negative information; and gives consumers the right to know what credit bureau provided the report when they are turned down for credit.

Fair Credit Billing Act (1975): Federal law that covers credit card billing problems. It applies to all open-end credit accounts (i.e. credit cards and overdraft checking). It states that consumers should send a written billing error notice to the creditor within 60 days (after receipt of first bill containing an error), which the creditor must acknowledge in 30 days. The creditor must investigate and may not damage a consumer's credit rating while a dispute is pending.

Fair Debt Collection Practices Act (1978): Federal law that prohibits debt collectors from engaging in unfair, deceptive or abusive practices when collecting debts. Collectors must send a written notice telling the name of the creditor and the amount owed; may not contact consumer if he or she disputes in writing within 30 days (unless collector furnishes proof of the debt); must identify themselves on the phone and can call only between 8 am and 9 pm unless a consumer agrees to another time; and cannot call consumers at work if they are told not to.

Equal Credit Opportunity Act (1975): Federal law that ensures that consumers are given an equal chance to receive credit. The law prohibits discrimination on the basis of gender, race, marital status, religion, national origin, age or receipt of public assistance. Lenders cannot ask about your plans for having children or refuse to consider consistently received alimony or child support payments as income. If you are denied credit, you have a legal right to know why.

Truth in Lending Act (1969): Federal law that mandates disclosure of information about the cost of credit. Both the finance charge (i.e. all charges to borrow money, including interest) and the annual percentage rate or APR (i.e. the percentage cost of credit on a yearly basis) must be displayed prominently on forms and statements used by creditors. The law provides criminal penalties for willful violators, as well as civil remedies. It also protects you against unauthorized use of your credit card. If it is lost or stolen, the maximum amount you have to pay is $50.

Fair Credit and Charge Card Disclosure Act (1989): A part of the Truth in Lending Act that mandates a box on credit card applications that describes key features and cost (i.e. APR, grace period for purchases, minimum finance charge, balance calculation method, annual fees, transaction fees for cash advances and penalty fees such as over the limit fees and late payment fees).

Credit life: Insurance that pays for financed items or purchases in the event of your death.

Credit report: Report showing your payment history.

Credit union: Nonprofit cooperatives of members with some type of common bond (i.e. employer) that provide a wide array of financial services, often at a lower cost than banks.

Curb appeal: The appearance of a home from the street.

Currency: Money.

Custodian: One who is responsible for an account listed in a minor's name.

Day trading: Establishing and liquidating the same position or positions within one day's trading.

Debit card: Linked with your checking account, this is a tool used to make purchases (not to be confused with a credit card).

Debt consolidation: Combining all debts into one lower monthly payment, thus extending the terms in most cases.

Debt snowball: Listing your debts smallest to largest and paying the minimum on all of them, then attacking the smallest with extra money that is available.

Debt-free fund: A fund used to buy your children a house when they get married with a condition: they take what would have been a house payment and invest it.

Deductible: The amount you pay to an insurance company before they begin paying.

Deed: The legal document conveying title to a property.

Deflation: A broad, overall drop in the price of goods and services; the opposite of the more-common inflation.

Delinquency: Short for "deed in lieu of foreclosure," this conveys title to the lender when the borrower is in default and wants to avoid foreclosure. The lender may or may not cease foreclosure activities if a borrower asks to provide a deed-in-lieu. Regardless of whether the lender accepts the deed-in-lieu, the avoidance and non-repayment of debt will most likely show on a credit history. What a deed-in-lieu may prevent is having the documents preparatory to a foreclosure being recorded and becoming a matter of public record.

Delivery: The action by which an underlying commodity, security, cash value or delivery instrument covering a contract is tendered and received by the contract holder. In most instances, the delivery of the actual underlying is rare; contracts are typically closed before settlement.

Depreciation: A decline in the value of property; the opposite of appreciation.

Direct deposit service: A service that electronically transfers all or part of any recurring payment, including dividends, paychecks, pensions and Social Security payments directly into a shareholder's account.

Direct transfer: Movement of tax-deferred retirement plan money from one qualified plan or custodian to another. No immediate tax liabilities or penalties are incurred, but there is an IRS reporting requirement.

Disability insurance: An insurance policy that insures a worker in the event of an occupational mishap resulting in disability. Insurance benefits compensate the injured worker for lost pay.

Discipline: The key to wealth building; you must be consistent over time.

Discount points: In the mortgage industry, this term is usually used only in reference to government loans, meaning FHA and VA loans. Discount points refer to any "points" paid in addition to the 1 percent loan origination fee. A "point" is 1 percent of the loan amount.

Disposable income: Amount of money left over after all necessities and expenses are paid.

Diversification: To spread around, thus lowering one's risk; spreading your money among different classes of financial assets and among the securities of many issuers.

Dividend: Stock profits that are paid out to shareholders.

Dividend distribution: Payment of income to mutual fund shareholders from interest or dividends generated by the fund's investments.

Dollar-cost averaging: Investing regular sums of money at regular intervals regardless of whether security prices are moving up or down.

Down payment: The part of the purchase price of a property that the buyer pays in cash and does not finance with a mortgage.

Earned income: Payment received for work, such as wages, salaries, commissions and tips.

Educational Savings Account (ESA): This is an after-tax college fund that grows tax-free. You may put up to $2,000 per year per child in this account depending on your annual income.

Elimination period: The amount of time that lapses after your disability and before the insurance company begins to pay you.

Emergency fund: Three to six months of expenses in readily available cash.

Employee benefit: Something of value that an employee receives in addition to a wage or salary.

Examples include health insurance, life insurance, discounted childcare and subsidized meals at the company cafeteria.

Employer-sponsored retirement savings program: Tax-deferred savings plans offered by employers that provides a federal tax deduction, tax-deferral of contributions and earning, and employer matching. They include 401(k) plans for corporate employees, 403(b) plans for employees of schools and nonprofit organizations, and Section 457 plans for state and local government employees.

Employer-sponsored savings plan: A government-approved program through which an employer can assist workers in building their personal retirement funds.

Empowerment: To gain strength emotionally and spiritually.

Entrepreneur: A person who starts a business.

Envelope system: A series of envelopes used to store cash for planned monthly expenses. This is a self-imposed discipline tool to assist people in managing their monthly finances (i.e. putting a set amount of money into a "food" envelope to spend only on "food" for that month).

Equity: Your ownership portion of an item.

Estate sale: Glorified yard sale with more items and higher prices. Usually a great place for negotiating.

Exchange privilege: The right to exchange shares in one fund for shares in another fund within the same fund family, typically at no charge or for a nominal fee.

Expense: The cost of a good or service.

Expense ratio: The percentage of a fund's average net assets used to pay annual fund expenses. The expense ratio takes into account management fees, administrative fees and any 12-b marketing fees.

Federal Deposit Insurance Corporation (FDIC): A federal institution that insures bank deposits.

Federal Housing Administration (FHA): Federally sponsored agency chartered in 1934 whose stock is currently owned by savings institutions across the United States. The agency buys residential mortgages that meet certain requirements, sells these mortgages in packages, and insures the lenders against loss.

Federal Insurance Contributions Act (FICA): Government legislation that funds Social Security.

Federal Reserve System: The monetary authority of the U.S. established in 1913 and governed by the Federal Reserve Board located in Washington, D.C. The system includes 12 Federal Reserve Banks and is authorized to regulate monetary policy in the U.S., as well as to supervise Federal Reserve Member Banks, bank holding companies, international operations of U.S. banks, and U.S. operations of foreign banks.

Fee table: A table placed near the front of a mutual fund's prospectus, disclosing and illustrating the expenses and fees a shareholder will incur.

Financial goals: Short, immediate, and long-term goals that require money and guide a person's financial plans and savings decisions.

Financial plan: A plan of action that allows a person to meet not only their immediate needs but also their long-term goals.

Financial resources: Financial assets that can be accessed when necessary.

Financing: To buy an item with credit; paying over time.

Finite: Having a beginning and an end. Money is finite; it has limits.

Fiscal: Having to do with money.

Fiscal year (FY): Accounting period covering 12 consecutive months over which a company determines earnings and profits. The fiscal year serves as a period of reference for the company and does not necessarily correspond to the calendar year.

Fixed annuity: A type of annuity that guarantees a certain rate of return, for example 6 percent. These are usually low and are not recommended for long-term wealth building.

Fixed income securities: Investments, such as bonds, which provide current income from a fixed schedule of interest payments. While the level of income offered by these securities is predetermined and usually stable, their market value may fluctuate.

Fixed Rate: An interest rate that does not change over time.

Floor Plan: The basic layout of a home.

Forbearance: A postponement of loan payments, granted by a lender or creditor, for a temporary period of time. This is done to give the borrower time to make up for overdue payments.

Foreclosure: Process by which the holder of a mortgage seizes the property of a homeowner who has not made interest and/or principal payments on time as stipulated in the mortgage contract.

Fraud: A seller's intentional deception of a buyer which is illegal.

Free spirit: One who thinks, "Everything will work out fine."

Front-end load: A sales commission or load that is paid when shares of a mutual fund are purchased.

Fund family: A group of mutual funds sponsored by the same organization, often offering exchange privileges between funds and combined account statements for multiple funds.

Futures: A term used to designate all contracts covering the sale of financial instruments or physical commodities for future delivery on a commodity exchange.

Garnishee: A court-ordered settlement that allows a lender to take monies owed directly from a borrower's paycheck.

Global fund: A mutual fund that invests anywhere in the world.

Government transfer payments: Payments by governments, such as Social Security, veteran's benefits and welfare to people who do not supply current goods, services or labor in exchange for these payments.

Grace Period: A time period during which a borrower can pay the full balance of credit due and not incur any finance charges.

Gratuity: An amount paid beyond what's required usually to express satisfaction with service quality. Also called a tip.

Gross income: A person's total income prior to exclusions and deductions.

Gross National Product (GNP): Measures an economy's total income. It is equal to GDP plus the income abroad accruing to domestic residents minus income generated in domestic market accruing to non-residents.

Growth and income mutual fund: These are funds that buy stocks in larger, more established companies. They also contain medium-sized companies or growth stocks. Also called a large-cap fund.

Growth stock mutual fund: These are funds that buy stock in companies that are medium in size. They have grown and are still expanding. Also called a mid-cap fund.

Guaranteed renewable: This means if you have a 20-year policy, the insurance has to provide coverage after 20 years regardless of your health. It will only be more expensive because you are older.

Health insurance: Covers you in the event of illness or injury.

Hoarding: Being greedy with an item, such as money.

Home Equity Loan (HEL): Borrowing money using the equity from your home as collateral. A credit line offered by mortgage lenders allowing a homeowner a second mortgage that uses the equity present in the customer's account as collateral.

Home inspector: An individual who inspects homes for defects prior to the closing of a home sale to insure the buyer or lender's investment.

Home warranty: An agreement that ensures the structural soundness of a home.

Homeowner's insurance: Insurance that covers a loss due to damage, theft or injury within your home.

House poor: Having a house payment that is so high that it limits you in your ability to maintain it.

Impulse purchase: To buy an item without thinking about it.

Income: Earnings from work or investment. Also called compensation.

Income fund: A mutual fund that invests in bonds and stocks with higher-than-average dividends.

Income risk: The possibility that income from a mutual fund or other investment will decline, either as a fund's assets are reinvested or when a fixed income investment matures and is replaced with a lower-yielding investment.

Index: A statistical benchmark designed to reflect changes in financial markets or the economy. In investing, indexes are used to measure changes in segments of the stock and bond markets and as standards against which fund managers and investors can measure the performance of their investment portfolios.

Index fund: A mutual fund that seeks to match the performance of a predetermined market benchmark or index.

Individual Retirement Account (IRA): A tax-deferred account for individuals with earned income and their non-income-producing spouses. Investments earning within an IRA are not taxed until money is withdrawn from an account. Contributions to an IRA may be deductible for income tax purposes.

Inflation: The rate at which the general level of prices for goods and services is rising. A broad, overall rise in the price of goods and services; the opposite of deflation.

Inflation hedge: Helps one to keep up with the rising cost of inflations. Real estate can be a great inflation hedge.

Integrity: Having to do with a person's honesty and moral attributes.

Interest: Money paid to savers and investors by financial institutions, governments or corporations for the use of their money (Example: 2 percent interest on money held in a savings account).

Interest rate: The monthly effective rate of interest on a loan.

Interest rate risk: The risk that a security of mutual funds will decline in price because of changes in market interest rates.

Internal Revenue Service (IRS): The federal agency responsible for the collection of federal taxes, including personal and corporate taxes, Social Security taxes, and excise and gift taxes.

International stock mutual fund: A mutual fund that contains international or overseas companies.

Investing: The process of setting money aside to increase wealth overtime and accumulate funds for long-term financial goals.

Investment: Where one would put their money for long-term growth for a suggested minimum of five years.

Investment advisor/manager: The individual who manages a portfolio of investments. Also called a portfolio manager or money manager.

Investment horizon: The length of time you expect to keep a sum of money invested.

Investment objective: A mutual fund's performance goal, such as long-term capital appreciation, high current income or tax-exempt income.

Investors: People investing in securities, such as stocks and bonds, to achieve long-term financial goals.

Job: A regular activity performed in exchange for payment, especially as one's trade, occupation or profession.

Land survey: A land survey is done to show one's property lines.

Large-cap fund: These types of funds contain large, well-established companies.

Lease: A long-term rental agreement and a form of secured, long-term debt.

Level term: This means you pay the same amount for the entire term of the policy.

Liability: Covers you in the event that someone brings a lawsuit against you due to injury on your property or as the result of an automobile accident.

Life insurance: Insurance that covers or replaces income lost due to death.

Liquidity: The availability of money. As there is more liquidity, there is typically less return. It is the quality of an asset that permits it to be converted quickly into cash without loss of value.

Load fund: A mutual fund that sells shares with a sales charge typically 4 to 8 percent of the net amount indicated. Some no-load funds also levy distribution fees permitted by Article 12b-1 of the Investment Company Act; these are typically 0.25 percent. A true no-load fund has no sales charge.

Loan: The temporary borrowing of a sum of money. If you borrow $1 million, you have taken out a loan for $1 million.

Loan to value (LTV): What you owe versus what you own. For example: a 70/30 LTV means that you owe 70 percent of the item's worth and own 30 percent of the items worth. Utilized with Private Mortgage Insurance (PMI).

Long-term care insurance: Covers the cost of nursing home or in-home care insurance. Recommended for people over the age of 60.

Long term coverage: Coverage for an extended period of time.

Loss: The negative difference between total revenue from a businesses or investment minus total expense.

Low-load fund: A mutual fund that charges a sales commission equal to 3 percent or less of the amount invested.

Lump sum savings: Saving money specifically for a purchase, such as a vacation, car, etc.

Management fee: The fee paid by a mutual fund to its investment advisor.

Manager risk: The possibility that a fund's investment advisor will do a poor job of selecting securities for the fund.

Market risk: The possibility that an investment will fall in value due to a general decline in the financial markets.

Maximum pay: The amount an insurance company will pay before you are dropped from coverage. With health insurance, keep at least a $1 million maximum pay.

Medical savings account (MSA): A health insurance plan for self-employed people containing a large deductible. Money saved in this account grows tax deferred. It can be used for medical care with no penalties, no taxes, and may be kept if unused.

Medicare: A federal government program of transfer payments for certain health care expenses for citizens 65 or older. The Social Security Administration manages this program.

Mid-cap fund: A mutual fund containing a group of medium-sized companies that are growing.

Money: Currency and coin that are guaranteed as legal tender by the government.

Money market fund: Utilized for borrowing and lending money for three years or less. It is a mutual fund that seeks to maintain a stable share price and to earn current income by investing in interest-bearing instruments with short-term (usually 90 days or less) maturities.

Money order: A financial instrument backed by a deposit at a certain firm (such as a bank) that can be easily converted into cash.

Mortgage: A loan secured by the collateral of some specified real estate property, which obligates the borrower to make a predetermined series of payments.

Mortgage life insurance: A life insurance policy that pays off the remaining balance of the insured person's mortgage at death.

Multiple Listings Service (MLS): A computer program realtors use to find prospective homes for their clients.

Murphy's Law: Anything that can happen will happen.

Mutual fund: Mutual funds are pools of money that are managed by an investment company. They offer investors a variety of goals, depending on the fund and its investment charter. Some funds seek to generate income on a regular basis. Others seek to preserve an investor's money. Still, others seek to invest in companies that are growing at a rapid pace. Funds can impose a sales charge (load) on investors when they buy or sell shares. Many funds these days are no-load and impose no sales charge. Mutual funds are investment companies regulated by the Investment Company Act of 1940. See open-end fund and closed-end fund.

Myth: Information that has been passed on and is not true.

Needs: Economic goods and services that are considered basic, such as food, clothing and shelter.

Negotiating: To bargain for a lower price.

Nerd: One who is picky about budgeting and numbers.

Nest egg: What you have to live on financially after your income from employment stops.

Net asset value (NAV): The market value of a mutual fund's total assets, less its liabilities, divided by the number of outstanding shares.

No-load mutual fund: An open-end investment company whose shares are sold without a sales charge. There can be other distribution charges, such as Article 12b-1 fees. A true no-load fund has neither a sales charge nor a distribution fee.

Objective: A goal or plan.

Obsolete: No longer produced or in existence; not accepted as current.

Occupational disability: Offers coverage in case you are unable to perform the job you were educated or trained to do.

Opportunity cost: Determining whether a purchase is a need or a want and realizing that once the money has been spent, it is gone.

Out-of-pocket: What YOU have to pay.

Owner financing: Instead of paying a mortgage company, you pay the owner, who finances the purchase of the home. This allows for lots of flexibility.

Paradigm: Your belief system; the way you see or perceive things.

Part-time job: A temporary job that allows you to supplement income.

Pawn shop: Retail establishment selling items that have been traded as security for a cash loan. This is a great place to find bargains.

Payroll deduction: An amount subtracted from a paycheck, as the government requires or the employee requests. Mandatory deductions include various taxes; voluntary deductions include loan payments or deposits into savings accounts.

Permanent disability: Disability that is ongoing.

Persistent: To be determined over time.

Points: See discount points.

Policy: Describes the type of coverage within an insurance agreement.

Portfolio: A list of your investments.

Portfolio transaction costs: The cost associated with buying and selling securities, including commissions on trades, dealer mark-ups on bonds, bid-asking spreads and any other miscellaneous expenses. These costs are not included in the expense ratio.

Preauthorized checking (PAC): Checking that is authorized by a payer in advance and written either by the payee or by the payee's bank and then deposited in the payee's bank account.

Preauthorized electronic debits (PAD): Debits to a bank account in advance by the payer. The payer's bank sends payment to the payee's bank through the Automated Clearing House (ACH) system.

Pre-paid tuition: Paying for college ahead of time by accumulating units of tuition. This is not recommended because your rate of return is only as much as the amount that tuition goes up as a result of inflation - on average about 6 to 7 percent.

Pre-tax retirement plan: A type of retirement plan where you put money in before taxes have been taken out, but you must pay taxes on the money at the time of withdrawal.

Premiums: The amount you pay monthly, quarterly, semi-annually or annually to purchase different types of insurance.

Principal: The original amount of money invested, excluding any interest of dividends. Also called the face value of a loan, not including interest.

Priority: Level of importance. Saving must become a priority and you should always pay for your priorities or necessities first.

Private mortgage insurance (PMI): Policy protecting the holder against loss resulting from default on a mortgage loan.

Pro rata: The percent of total debt each creditor represents; their share.

Proactive: To have a strong initiative; when one happens "to" things.

Procrastinating: To put off until later; waiting until the last minute.

Profit: The positive difference between total revenue from a business or investment minus the total expense.

Prospectus: An official document that contains information required by the Securities and Exchange Commission to describe a mutual fund.

Purchasing power: A measurement of the relative value of money in terms of the quality and quantity of goods and service it can buy. Inflation decreases purchasing power; deflation increases it.

Rate of return: The return on an investment expressed as a percentage of its cost. Also called yield.

Realtor: An intermediary who receives a commission for arranging and facilitating the sale of a property for a buyer or a seller. Also called a real estate broker or agent.

Reconcile: To work out. You should always reconcile your bank statement with your checkbook within 72 hours of receiving the statement.

Redemption fee: A fee charged by some mutual funds for selling (redeeming) shares.

Refunding: Sending in proofs of purchase to receive cash back or free gifts.

Reinvestment: Use of investment income or dividends to buy additional shares.

Rent: Periodic fee for the use of property.

Rental real estate: Buying real estate to rent out as an investment. Make sure you have plenty of cash before doing this.

Renter's insurance: Insurance that protects the possessions of one who rents a home or apartment.

Replacement cost: Pays what it would cost to replace your home and the contents.

Repo lot: A place where items that have been repossessed are offered for sale.

Resume: Personal and work history used for gaining employment.

Retailer: One who buys a product to resale.

Risk: The degree of uncertainty of return on an asset. In business, it is the likelihood of loss or reduced profit.

Risk management: Procedures to minimize the adverse effect of a possible financial loss by: 1) identifying potential sources of loss, 2) measuring the financial consequences of a loss occurring, and 3) using controls to minimize actual losses or their financial consequences.

Risk return ratio: Relationship of substantial reward corresponding to the amount of risk taken.

Risk tolerance: An investor's personal ability or willingness to endure declines in the prices of investments.

Rollover: Movement of a tax-deferred retirement plan's money from one qualified plan or custodian to another. No immediate tax liabilities or penalties are incurred, but there is an IRS reporting requirement.

Roth IRA: This is an after-tax investment where you have already paid tax on the money you are using, but the investment grows tax-free.

Royalty: Payment to someone for the right to use or sell his or her goods (i.e. paying an author based on sales of the book).

Rule of 72: A quick way to calculate the length of time it will take to double a sum of money. Divide 72 by the expected interest rate to determine the number of years (i.e. 72 divided by 8 percent = 9 years).

Rule of 78: Pre-payment penalty. In 90-days same-as-cash deals, this is the portion of the loan agreement which states that the entire loan amount plus the interest earned over the first 90 days becomes due immediately.

Salary: Payment for work, usually calculated in periods of a week or longer. Salary is usually tied to the completion of specific duties over a minimum number of hours. Also called wages.

Savings: The process of setting aside money until a future date instead of spending it today. The goal of savings is to provide funds for emergencies, short-term goals and investments.

Savings account: Accounts at financial institutions that allow regular deposits and withdrawals. The minimum required deposit, fees charged and interest rate paid varies among providers.

Savings bond: A bond is a certificate representing a debt. A U.S. savings bond is a loan to the government. The government agrees to repay the amount borrowed, with interest, to the bondholder. A government bond is issued in face value denominations from $50 to $10,000 with local and state tax-free interest and semi-annually adjusted interest rates.

Savings and loan associations (S and Ls): Financial institutions that provide loans and interest-bearing accounts. Accounts in federally chartered S and Ls are federally insured.

Sector fund: A mutual fund that invests its shareholder's money in a relatively narrow market sector (i.e. technology, energy, the internet or banking).

Self-esteem: One's attitude about themselves.

Self-insured: To insure one's self with personal assets.

Share: A piece of ownership in a company stock or mutual fund.

Short-term disability: Disability for a minimal period of time.

Short-term policy: Insurance policy that only covers a minimal amount of time.

Significant purchase: Anything over $300.

Simple interest: Interest credited daily, monthly, quarterly, semi-annually or annually on principle only, not previously credited interest.

Simple IRA: A salary deduction plan for retirement benefits provided by some small companies with less than 100 employees.

Simplified employee pension plan (SEP): A pension plan in which both the employee and the employer contribute to an individual retirement account. These are also available to the self-employed.

Single stock: Buying ownership in one company. The problem with single stocks is that they are not diversified; there is a high degree of risk in single stocks.

Sinking fund: Saving money to allow interest to work for you rather than against you.

Small-cap fund: A mutual fund that invests in companies whose market value is less than $1 billion. Mutual funds that buy and sell smaller more volatile companies. Also called aggressive growth stock mutual fund.

Social Security: A federal government program of transfer payments for retirement, disability or the loss of income from a parent or guardian. Funds come from tax on income, which is a payroll deduction labeled FICA.

Speculative: Purchasing risky investments that present the possibility of large profits but also pose a higher-than-average possibility of loss.

Stock markets:

National Association of Securities Dealers Automated Quotation System (NASDAQ): The electronic stock exchange run by the National Association of Securities Dealers for over-the-counter trading. Established in 1971, it is America's fastest growing stock market and a leader in trading foreign securities and technology shares as well. The NASDAQ uses market makers who trade for their own account and profit on the spread between the bid and ask prices. Although once the province of smaller companies, NASDAQ today is where many leading companies are traded, including Microsoft, Intel, MCI, Amgen, Cisco Systems, Nordstrom, Oracle, McCormick, SAFECO Insurance, Sun Microsystems, T. Rowe Price, Tyson Foods and Northwest Airlines.

New York Stock Exchange (NYSE): The New York Stock Exchange traces it origins back more than 200 years to the signing of the Buttonwood Agreement by 24 New York City stockbrokers and merchants in 1792. The NYSE utilizes a trading floor for traditional exchanges where buyers and sellers meet directly - that is, brokers representing investors on each side of the transaction come together on price. Centuries of growth and innovation later, the NYSE remains the world's foremost securities marketplace.

Stocks: Securities that represent part ownership or equity in a corporation. Each share is a claim on its proportionate stake in the corporation's assets and profits, some of which may be paid out as dividends.

Stop-loss: Your total out-of-pocket expense for health insurance. Once reached, insurance will pay 100 percent.

Stuffitis: The wrong priority of "stuff" in your life; to be overly materialistic.

Take-home pay: The amount of money one has available after taxes have been taken out of his or her pay. Total wages, salary, commissions and/or bonuses minus payroll deductions.

Tax: A government fee on businesses and individual income, activities, products or services.

Tax credit: An amount that a taxpayer who meets certain criteria can subtract from tax owed. Examples include a credit for earned income below a certain limit and for qualified post-secondary school expenses. See tax deduction and tax exemption.

Tax deductible: The effect of creating a tax deduction such as charitable contributions and mortgage interest.

Tax deduction: An expense that a taxpayer is allowed to deduct from taxable income. Examples include deductions from home mortgage interest and for charitable fights. See tax credit and tax exemption.

Tax-deferred income: Dividends, interest and unrealized capital gains on investments in an account such as a qualified retirement plan where income is not subject to taxation until a withdrawal is made. Investments where taxes due on the amount invested and/or its earnings are postponed until funds are withdrawn, usually at retirement.

Tax-exempt (tax-free): Investment earnings that are free from tax liability.

Tax exemptions: An amount that a taxpayer who meets certain criteria can subtract from a taxable income. Examples include exemptions for each dependant or life insurance proceeds. See tax credit and tax deduction.

Tax-favored dollars: Money that is working for you, either tax-deferred or tax-free, within a retirement plan.

Taxable income: Income subject to tax; total income adjusted for deductions, exemptions and credits.

Term insurance: Life insurance for a specified period of time. This is less expensive than cash value and what is recommended for life insurance coverage.

Time poverty: Having very little time to manage daily activities.

Time value of money: Comparison of a lump sum of money (or a series of equal payments) between two different time periods (present and future), assuming a specified interest rate and time period. (Reference: The Time Value of Money by Clayton and Spivey).

Tip: An amount paid beyond what's required, usually to express satisfaction with service quality. Also called gratuity.

Title insurance: Insurance policy that protects a policyholder from future challenges to the title claim of a property that may result in loss of the property.

Total return: The change in percentage over a particular period in the value of an investment, including any income from the investment and any change in its market value.

Track record: The past history of something. With investments, check at least the 5- to 10-year track record.

Transfer payments: See government transfer payments.

Turnover rate: A measure of a mutual fund's trading activity. Turnover is calculated by taking the lesser of the fund's total purchases or total sales of securities (not counting securities with maturities under one year) and dividing by the average monthly assets (i.e. a turnover rate of 50 percent means that during a year, a fund has sold and replaced securities with a value equal to 50 percent of the fund's average net assets).

Umbrella: Provides extra liability. Once your assets are above $200,000, you should consider this.

Underwriter: A firm, usually an investment bank, that buys an issue of securities from a company and resells it to investors. In general, a party that guarantees the proceeds to the firm from a security sale, thereby in effect taking ownership of the securities.

Unearned income: Money received for which no exchange was made, such as a gift.

Uniform Gifts to Minors Act (UGMA): Legislation that provides a tax-effective manner of transferring property to minors without the complications of trusts or guardianship restrictions.

Uniform Transfers to Minors Act (UTMA): A law similar to the Uniform Gifts to Minors Act that extends the definition of gifts to include real estate, paintings, royalties and patents.

Universal life: Similar to cash value life insurance but projects better returns. This is not recommended as the type of life insurance to purchase.

Unrealized capital gain/loss: An increase or decrease in the value of a stock or other security (mutual fund) that is not realized because the security has not yet been sold for a gain or loss.

VA loan: Designed to benefit veterans; allows for a true zero-down purchase.

Value fund: A mutual fund that emphasizes stocks of companies whose growth prospects are generally regarded as sub-par by the market. Reflecting these market expectations, the prices of value stocks typically are below average in comparison with such factors as revenue, earnings, book value and dividends.

Value systems: One's priorities and things deemed important.

Variable annuity: An annuity that has a varying rate of return based on the mutual funds in which you have invested. This is better than the fixed annuity.

Variable life: Similar to cash value life insurance, but it will buy into mutual funds to project better returns. This is not recommended as the type of life insurance to buy.

Viatical: Of or relating to a contractual arrangement in which a business buys life insurance policies from terminally ill patients for a percentage of the face value.

Vocation: What you do for a living; your "calling."

Volatility: The fluctuations in market value of a mutual fund or other security. The greater a fund's volatility, the wider the fluctuations between high and low prices.

Wage: Payment for work, usually as calculated in periods of an hour rather than longer. Also called salary.

Walk-away power: In negotiating, this is the ability to walk away from a purchase.

Wants: Desires for economic goods or services, not necessarily accompanied by the power to satisfy them.

Wealth: Accumulated assets such as money and/or possessions, often as a result of saving and investing.

Whole life insurance: This is more expensive than term insurance in order to fund a savings plan within the insurance. This is not recommended as the type of life insurance you need. Also called cash value insurance.

Win-win deal: Setting up a negotiation where both parties benefit.

Work ethic: How motivated you are in your work.

Yield: The annualized rate at which an investment earns income; expressed as a percentage of the investment's current price. Also called rate of return.

Zero-coupon bond: A bond in which no periodic coupon is paid over the life of the contract. Instead, both the principal and the interest are paid at the maturity date.

Zero-based budget: A cash flow plan where you spend every dollar on paper before the month begins.